A COURSE IN TELECOMMUNICATION ENGINEERING

Dr. Michael Olorunfunmi Kolawole

B.Eng., MEnvSt, Ph.D.

S. CHAND & COMPANY LTD.

(AN ISO 9001 : 2000 COMPANY)

RAM NAGAR, NEW DELHI - 110 055

S. CHAND & COMPANY LTD.

(An ISO 9001 : 2000 Company)

Head Office: 7361, RAM NAGAR, NEW DELHI - 110 055
Phone: 23672080-81-82, 9899107446, 9911310888
Fax: 91-11-23677446
Shop at: **schandgroup.com**; e-mail: **info@schandgroup.com**

Branches :

AHMEDABAD	: 1st Floor, Heritage, Near Gujarat Vidhyapeeth, Ashram Road, **Ahmedabad** - 380 014, Ph: 27541965, 27542369, ahmedabad@schandgroup.com
BANGALORE	: No. 6, Ahuja Chambers, 1st Cross, Kumara Krupa Road, **Bangalore** - 560 001, Ph: 22268048, 22354008, bangalore@schandgroup.com
BHOPAL	: 238-A, M.P. Nagar, Zone 1, **Bhopal** - 462 011, Ph: 4274723. bhopal@schandgroup.com
CHANDIGARH	: S.C.O. 2419-20, First Floor, Sector - 22-C (Near Aroma Hotel), **Chandigarh** -160 022, Ph: 2725443, 2725446, chandigarh@schandgroup.com
CHENNAI	: 152, Anna Salai, **Chennai** - 600 002, Ph: 28460026, chennai@schandgroup.com
COIMBATORE	: Plot No. 5, Rajalakshmi Nagar, Peelamedu, **Coimbatore** -641 004, (M) 09444228242, coimbatore@schandgroup.com
CUTTACK	: 1st Floor, Bhartia Tower, Badambadi, **Cuttack** - 753 009, Ph: 2332580; 2332581, cuttack@schandgroup.com
DEHRADUN	: 1st Floor, 20, New Road, Near Dwarka Store, **Dehradun** - 248 001, Ph: 2711101, 2710861, dehradun@schandgroup.com
GUWAHATI	: Pan Bazar, **Guwahati** - 781 001, Ph: 2738811, 2735640 guwahati@schandgroup.com
HYDERABAD	: Sultan Bazar, **Hyderabad** - 500 195, Ph: 24651135, 24744815, hyderabad@schandgroup.com
JAIPUR	: A-14, Janta Store Shopping Complex, University Marg, Bapu Nagar, **Jaipur** - 302 015, Ph: 2719126, jaipur@schandgroup.com
JALANDHAR	: Mai Hiran Gate, **Jalandhar** - 144 008, Ph: 2401630, 5000630, jalandhar@schandgroup.com
JAMMU	: 67/B, B-Block, Gandhi Nagar, **Jammu** - 180 004, (M) 09878651464
KOCHI	: Kachapilly Square, Mullassery Canal Road, Ernakulam, **Kochi** - 682 011, Ph: 2378207, cochin@schandgroup.com
KOLKATA	: 285/J, Bipin Bihari Ganguli Street, **Kolkata** - 700 012, Ph: 22367459, 22373914, kolkata@schandgroup.com
LUCKNOW	: Mahabeer Market, 25 Gwynne Road, Aminabad, **Lucknow** - 226 018, Ph: 2626801, 2284815, lucknow@schandgroup.com
MUMBAI	: Blackie House, 103/5, Walchand Hirachand Marg, Opp. G.P.O., **Mumbai** - 400 001, Ph: 22690881, 22610885, mumbai@schandgroup.com
NAGPUR	: Karnal Bag, Model Mill Chowk, Umrer Road, **Nagpur** - 440 032, Ph: 2723901, 2777666 nagpur@schandgroup.com
PATNA	: 104, Citicentre Ashok, Govind Mitra Road, **Patna** - 800 004, Ph: 2300489, 2302100, patna@schandgroup.com
PUNE	: 291/1, Ganesh Gayatri Complex, 1st Floor, Somwarpeth, Near Jain Mandir, **Pune** - 411 011, Ph: 64017298, pune@schandgroup.com
RAIPUR	: Kailash Residency, Plot No. 4B, Bottle House Road, Shankar Nagar, **Raipur** - 492 007, Ph: 09981200834, raipur@schandgroup.com
RANCHI	: Flat No. 104, Sri Draupadi Smriti Apartments, East of Jaipal Singh Stadium, Neel Ratan Street, Upper Bazar, **Ranchi** - 834 001, Ph: 2208761, ranchi@schandgroup.com
VISAKHAPATNAM	: Plot No. 7, 1st Floor, Allipuram Extension, Opp. Radhakrishna Towers, Seethammadhara North Extn., **Visakhapatnam** - 530 013, (M) 09347580841, visakhapatnam@schandgroup.com

First Edition 2010

ISBN : 81-219-3263-7   **Code : 10 422**

PRINTED IN INDIA
*By Rajendra Ravindra Printers Pvt. Ltd., 7361, Ram Nagar, New Delhi -110 055
and published by S. Chand & Company Ltd., 7361, Ram Nagar, New Delhi -110 055.*

Dedication

To Dr Marjorie Helen Kolawole, my wife and best confidant, who always inspires and brings the best out of me. With my fondest love and eternal gratitude. The sweetest of women!

Also, to my children with profound joy and love:

Oluseyi Francis Kolawole

Aderemi Matthew Kolawole

Tolulope Seun Kolawole

Olawale Olumide Kolawole

PREFACE

This monograph is written to provide basic information to telecommunications engineering students and practitioners, as well as to applied scientists who would want to know the principles governing the daily operational tools that they take for granted, and importantly to gain more knowledge.

As an educator and practitioner in the fields of information and communications technology, I have written this monograph with balanced theoretical knowledge and practical experience to stimulate inquiring mind and help the readers to gain much more understanding of subject matter, including relevant international telecommunication standards.

The monograph has been structured into ten chapters to identify and describe the principles that govern the structure and development of telecommunication networks, particularly the way in which various components interact. Students and practitioners will have an adequate appreciation of the purpose and mode of operation of the public telephone network, as well as comprehending the technical issues in the design of switching systems and networks. Practice questions are given at the end of each chapter to test the reader's understandability of the preceding chapter as well as gearing himself or herself to applying the gained principles in the real world. This technique serves two purposes: helping the reader to become confident and self-critical at the same time. This acts as a catalyst to encourage the reader in correcting misconceptions or deepening his/her understanding of the concept or skill at hand.

Chapter 1 introduces the fundamentals of relevance to the field of telecommunication engineering. Afterwards, a series of chapters is embarked on in which the subject treatment is more detailed and focused, commencing with network planning and design which Chapter 2 discusses with a particular reference to a public telephone network without stressing the historical undertones. Chapter 3 looks at a public telephone network switching arrangement, telecommunications structure, links, network standards and grade and quality of services.

The process of establishing a successful connection between any two exchanges in a network depends on the routing schemes in place, which chapter 4 explains. Chapter 5 discusses signalling system. A telephone network requires an effective signalling system to transmit orders and information, which is akin to the human nervous system. With digital switching now a mature technology in circuit-switched networks, Chapter 6 examines the theory of the switching matrix and switching architectures such as space and time switching, and associated switching fabrics.

An overview of modern communications satellites is given in chapter 7, while the engineering principle behind a mobile telecommunications system is covered in Chapter 8. There are aspects of satellite communication engineering, like other topics discussed in this monograph, that require specialist treatment, which this monograph is not well equipped to handle. Wherever required, sufficient references are given.

Public telecommunications networks are designed to accommodate the offered traffic intensity with only a small loss. The probabilistic systems analysis concepts have been applied in Chapter 9 to measure this performance loss, as well as investigating the network throughput, grade of service, the average traffic flow supportable by a base station and/or mobile switching centre, and channel load factor. In the application of these probabilistic systems analysis concepts, the chapter bypasses mathematically rigorous proofs and relies instead on simpler intuitive explanations.

Chapter 10 reflects on the future manufacturing sciences and applicable technologies that may shift or influence the way we currently handle and transport telecommunication devices and information.

Michael Olorunfunmi Kolawole

ACKNOWLEDGMENTS

I am indebted to my family for their unfailing support writing and transferring knowledge to a wider audience when, at times, I could have spent the precious time with them. For their love and belief in me, I am eternally grateful.

My thanks also go to my colleague, Stuart Uhlhorn, who is always available to provide software support whenever requested, thus ensuring better presentation.

NOTATIONS

The symbols have been chosen as carefully as possible to prevent confusion. In a few instances, same symbol was used. When this occurs, a clear distinction is made in their meaning and where used in the text is indicated.

Symbol	Meaning
A	traffic intensity or offered traffic flow to the base station
B	Bandwidth
$B(M, A)$	traffic congestion or the probability of a network capable of supporting M simultaneous calls being fully occupied, given that the offered traffic flow is A
C	system capacity or rate of information transmission
c	speed of light in free space
c_k	Kasami-code
$C_{message}$	C-message noise meter reading
f	propagation frequency
F_a	future amount of money
H_{2n}	Hadamard matrix of $2n$ where n is positive integer
L	route length
LR	Loudness ratings
$P_{ITU\text{-}T}$	Psophometer reading
P_k	probability of simultaneous calls present at the base station
P_v	present value of money invested
s	signal amplitude levels
S_i	sensitivity at frequency F_i of the electro-acoustic path
T_d	average call duration
r_b	original bit rate
W_i	weighting coefficient
y_s	charge to the subscriber
β_m	flagfall or connection fee
ε_o	permittivity in vacuum
λ	wavelength (or average data arrival rate as in Chapter 9)
μ	server or buffer
μ_o	permeability in vacuum

NOTATIONS

The symbols have been chosen as carefully as possible to prevent confusion. In a few instances, same symbol was used. When this occurs, a clarification is made in that meaning and where used in the text symbol, etc.

Symbol	Meaning
A	traffic measure or offered traffic flow to the base station.
B	Bandwidth
$B(M, A)$	traffic congestion or the probability of a network capable of supporting M simultaneous calls being fully occupied, given that the offered traffic flow is A.
C	system capacity or rate of information transmission
c	speed of light in free space
C_i	Kasami code
C_{noise}	Coverage noise meter reading
f_p	propagation frequency
h	minimum amount of money
$m(t)$	Hadamard matrix of 2^n where n is positive integer
l	path length
LR	Loudness rating
P_{baro}	Barometer reading
P_s	probability of small number cells present at the base station
P	present value of money invested
s	signal amplitude in dB
S	sensitivity at frequency f_c of the electroacoustic path
T_a	average call duration
T_c	original bit rate
W	weighting coefficient
w	charge to the subscriber
L_c	flagfall or connection fee
ε_0	permittivity in vacuum
λ_a	wavelength (or average task arrival rate as in Chapter 9)
p	server or buffer
μ_0	permeability in vacuum

CONTENTS

1

INTRODUCTION TO TELECOMMUNICATION PRINCIPLES

This chapter provides a brief overview of the general concepts associated with telecommunication engineering including transmission and devices.

1.1 TELECOMMUNICATION: WHAT IS IT?

Literally, telecommunication means communicating over long distances. As such, telecommunication can be defined as sending information by electrical means over distances, which can be greater than the normal range of the senses [Smith, 1969]. In technical terms, telecommunication could be said as the transmission of signals (a time-varying quantity) over a distance for the purpose of communication-the exchange of information or passing of messages. In modern times, telecommunication process typically involves the sending of electromagnetic waves by electronic transmitters. For an encompassing definition, telecommunication is any transmission, emission, or reception of signs, signals, writings, images, sounds, or information of any nature by wire, radio, visual, or other electromagnetic systems.

In telecommunication, transmission is the forwarding of signal traffic (such as a series of data units; for example blocks, messages, or frames) over distances by any means, such as by telegraph, telephone, radio, television, or facsimile via any medium, for instance wire, coaxial cable, microwave link, optical fibre, or satellite link. Nearly all modern transmission is digital.

Today in many parts of the world, telecommunication is widespread and devices that assist the process of communication, such as the television, radio, facsimile, and telephone are common. There are also many networks that connect these devices, including computer networks, public telephone networks, radio and television networks. Computer communication across the internet is one of many examples of telecommunication.

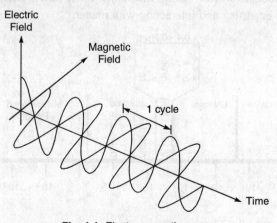

Fig. 1.1. Electromagnetic wave

An electromagnetic wave is self-propagating wave in space formed when an electric field couples with a magnetic field as in Fig 1.1. The magnetic and electric fields are perpendicular to each other and to the direction of the wave. Since the wavy waveform, seen in Fig 1.1, keeps repeating itself and in motion, it is possible to measure the physical distance between matching points of adjacent cycles of the waveform. This distance is called the *wavelength*, λ. For electromagnetic waves, propagation may occur in a vacuum, in waveguides, as well as in a material medium. Light, microwaves, *x*-rays (*e.g.*, used in hospitals to produce images of the human body), and television (TV) and radio transmissions (*e.g.*, Police radar gun that is used to determine the speed of objects, or signals that travel between transmitting and receiving antennae) are all kinds of electromagnetic waves.

The speed of an electromagnetic wave in space is equal to the speed of light, c. Functionally represented by

$$c = \frac{1}{\sqrt{\mu_o \varepsilon_o}} \approx 3 \times 10^8 \text{ m/s} \tag{1.1}$$

where μ_o = permeability = $4\pi \times 10^{-7}$ (H/m)

      ε_o = permittivity = 8.854×10^{-12} (F/m)

The 'zero' subscript in the permeability and permittivity symbols shows that the functions are associated only to vacuum.

Permeability is the degree of magnetization of material in response to a magnetic field. It has a unit of Henries per metre (H/m). Whereas, permittivity shows how electric field is affected by dielectric medium. It has a unit of Faradays per metre (F/m). The wavelength, λ, can also be estimated as

$$\lambda = ct = \frac{c}{f} \tag{1.2}$$

where *t* is the time (in sec.) measured between matching points of adjacent cycles of the waveform, or the inverse of the propagation frequency, *f*, of the waveform. Frequency is the number of complete *cycles* per second. The unit of frequency is hertz (Hz). One Hz is one cycle per second.

As seen in Fig. 1.2, an electromagnetic spectrum is a group of types of electromagnetic radiation. Electromagnetic radiation, EMR, is a form of energy that reveals its presence by the observable effects it produces when it strikes the matter. EMR carries energy and momentum, and spreads out as it goes, imparting and interacting with matter.

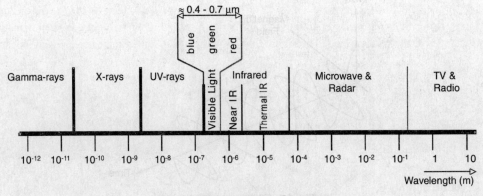

Fig. 1.2. Electromagnetic Spectrum

EMR is classified into types according to the frequency of the wave: these types include, in order of increasing frequency; TV and radio waves, microwaves and radar, infrared radiation, visible light, ultraviolet radiation, X-rays and gamma rays. The cosmic rays are at the other end of the spectrum. Hotter, more energetic objects and events create higher energy radiation than cool objects. Only extremely hot objects or particles moving at very high velocities can create high-energy radiation like X-rays and gamma rays. The rate of this energy is called *radiant flux*. Judicious use of this energy enables remote sensors to detect presence.

1.2 TELEGRAPHY AND TELEPHONY

In *telephony*, messages are sent and received in spoken form using instruments like telephones. In *telegraphy*, written messages are sent and received in written form over a distance using instruments like fax (short name for facsimile). The operation of a telephone or fax machine is strictly specified by the International Telecommunications Union—Telecommunications Sector (ITU-T)—formerly *Comit´e Consultatif International de T´el´egraphie et de T´el´ephonie* (*i.e.*, International Telegraph and Telephone Consultative Committee, CCITT). This committee sets the standards thereby allowing different manufactures and instruments in different countries to communicate with each other. More is said about ITU in Section 1.6.

1.2.1 Principle of Telephone and Facsimile

1.2.1.1 *Facsimile*

A facsimile (or fax) machine electrically breaks up a document into pixels (very small pieces of *picture elements*) and sends them one by one to another fax by way of a phone line. The density of each pixel is converted into an electric current, which is sent to the receiving fax machine (*i.e.*, receiver). The receiving fax puts the pixels together as it receives them, until a copy of the original is made.

During transmission the document is broken down into pixels (or picture elements) by reflecting the image of the document being scanned through a lens that is focused onto an optical unit, commonly referred to as a *charge-coupled device* (CCD). A CCD is basically an integrated circuit of photoelectric light sensors. The function of a CCD is to photoelectrically convert the image into different levels of electrical current based on the intensity of light of each pixel. The electrical signals are then modulated and sent over the phone line.

Modulation is the addition of an information signal (or picture signal) to an electronic or optical signal carrier, as demonstrated in Fig. 1.3. Any measurable property of such signal can be used to transmit information by changing this property in some known manner and then detecting those changes at the receiver end. The signal that is modulated is called the carrier signal, because

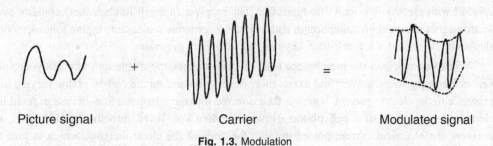

Picture signal   +   Carrier   =   Modulated signal

Fig. 1.3. Modulation

it carries the transmitted information from one end of the communication channel to the other end. For most of radio and telecommunication today, the carrier is alternating current in a given range of frequencies.

Typically, three types of modulation are used in fax equipment namely: amplitude modulation (AM), frequency modulation (FM) and phase modulation (PM). The most popular forms of modulation employed in digital communications are binary phase shift keying (BPSK), quadrature phase shift keying (QPSK), offset-quadrature phase shift keying (OQPSK) and 8-PSK. These modulation formats can be described in a general form as M-PSK modulation, where $M = 2^b$ bits, each symbol represents b bits, and where b is an integer 1, 2, 3. For more detail exposition on modulation including its types, formulation and development, the reader is advised to consult Kolawole (2002).

During reception the signal is demodulated and the electrical signals are sent to a printing device–which could be of any variety; thermal print head, bubble jet print head or laser printer. The image of the original document transmitted would then be created. Demodulation is the reverse of modulation, as seen in Fig. 1.4.

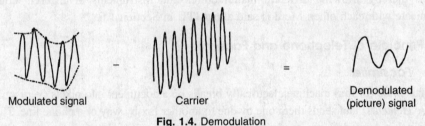

Modulated signal   Carrier   Demodulated
                                                                    (picture) signal

Fig. 1.4. Demodulation

The International Telecommunications Union—Telecommunications Sector (ITU-T) strictly specifies the operation of a fax machine. This committee sets the standards for all fax equipment thereby allowing different manufacturers of different sizes and types in different countries to communicate with each other. Facsimiles are broadly classified as follows:

- Group I (G_1) Old FM Transmission time: approx. 6 minutes.
- Group II (G_2) Transmission time: approx. 3 minutes.
- Group III (G_3) Transmission time: less then 1 minute.
- Group IV (G_4) Transmission time: approx. 10 seconds.

1.2.1.2 *Telephone*

A telephone is made of a transmitter (*i.e.*, mouthpiece) for transmission and a receiver (*i.e.*, earpiece) for reception; see Fig. 1.5. The transmitter (a microphone) consists of a metal diaphragm placed against grains of carbon. In a modern telephone, the carbon granules and loading coil are replaced with electronic circuit and amplifier. The receiver (a small loudspeaker) consists of an electromagnet mounted on a diaphragm and a circuit to generate a pleasant ringing tone. A modern telephone also includes a touch-tone keypad and frequency generator.

When you talk into the mouthpiece (*i.e.*, the transmitter), the diaphragm vibrates your voice (*i.e.*, as incoming sound waves) and exerts more or less pressure on the carbon grains varying their resistance to the electric current, which is then directed into the telephone line–in case of fixed line telephone, or antenna of a cell phone. However, when you listen into the earpiece (*i.e.*, the receiver), the electrical current passes through the coils of the electromagnet, which in turn the

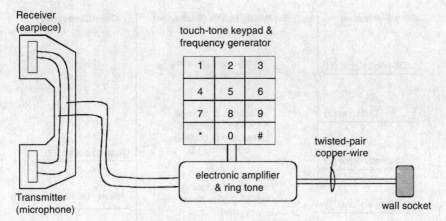

Fig. 1.5. Elements of a telephone

magnet makes the diaphragm vibrate—incidentally the sound waves are identical to those created by the incoming sound waves.

Speech consists of a complex combination of sound waves at a number of different frequencies from about 50 Hz to 10 KHz. To propagate across this frequency range would be too expensive. Consequently, for telephone systems, they are typically designed for a frequency range between 300 Hz and 3.4 KHz (that is, with a *bandwidth* of 3.1 KHz), which is sufficient for the transmitted words to be understood, and the talker's voice to be recognizable.

1.2.1.2.1 *Set up of a telephone call*

We take for granted the mechanism that facilitates the daily use of the telephone, in terms of the calling subscriber and the called subscriber. The sequential process is depicted in Fig. 1.6, and describes concisely as follows.

When a subscriber wishes to make a call, the telephone handset is lifted. This state is called an off-hook signal (or seize signal or calling signal), which informs the exchange that there is a call request.

Upon receiving the "off-hook" signal by the switching centre (exchange), the control system allocates some common equipment to the call and connects the necessary path. The exchange then reserves some dual tone (or multi-frequency) receivers to receive the dialled digits from a dual tone telephone set, shown in Fig. 1.5. More is said about the telephone exchanges in chapter 3, and switching mechanism in Chapter 6.

The control system then connects the dial tone (DT) to the calling subscriber to signal the ready state of receiving dialled digits.

Once the calling subscriber has received the dial tone, the calling subscriber dials the called subscriber number or dialled digits (also called the address digits, the address signal, or the register signal). The type of signalling used depends on the network; it is either the Dual Tone Multi-frequency (DTMF) signalling or the Decadic Pulse (DP) signalling.

Decadic Pulse Signalling or dial pulsing is defined as a momentary on-hook condition that causes loop making and breaking in the local loop. For this to occur, there must be an inter-digit pause (or period) (IDP) between two consecutive trains of pulses.

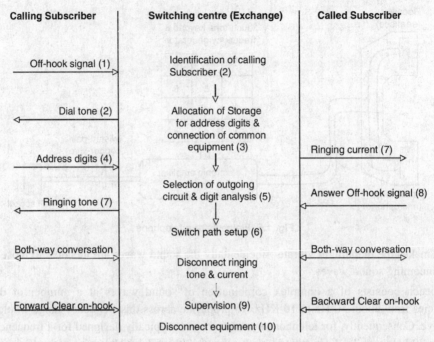

Fig. 1.6. Process of setting up a telephone call

The theoretical concept of DTMF is provided in Chapter 5. In the time being, the application of this concept is given here to give the reader a feel for the transmission process. When the calling subscriber presses a button on the touch-tone keypad, two tones (frequencies) are sent to the telephone exchange: one from the low frequency band (*e.g.*, 697 Hz, 770 Hz, 852 Hz, 941 Hz), and one from the high frequency band (*e.g.*, 1209 Hz, 1336 Hz, 1477 Hz, 1633 Hz). A major advantage of the DTMF is the speed, which is typically 50 ms duration of digit with a minimum inter-digit period of about 45 ms.

The address digits are analysed to determine whether it is a local call or an outgoing call. If it is a local call, the control system checks the status of the called subscriber. For example, if the called subscriber is engaged, a busy tone is sent to the caller. If the called subscriber is idle, the control system proceeds to next stage: by setting up a path between the calling and the called; *i.e.*, a forward signal—ringing signal of nominal voltage of 75 Vrms and 20 Hz frequency—is sent to give a ringing signal to the called subscriber. As well, a backward signal—a ringing tone—is sent to the calling subscriber informing the status of the call.

When the called subscriber picks up the handset, an off-hook signal is sent to the exchange. At this instance, the ringing current and ringing tone will be removed. A supervisory role is thus initiated by the exchange to detect any clear signal and to detect any three-party call request. If a clear signal is observed; that is, forward clear generated by calling subscriber and backward clear generated by called subscriber, the control system will release the path and disconnect all equipment.

If the control system identifies the call as an outgoing call in the digit analysis, it will hunt for a free trunk that is connected to the designating exchange (also called terminating exchange). This marking operation is called seize signal. The destination exchange will allocate storage and connect common equipment and then send back 'a proceed signal' to the send signal. The received address digits in the originating exchange will be sent to the designating exchange in which the digit analysis and path set up will be performed as described previously. More is said about telephone-digit-number assignment in Chapter 2, section 2.5.

In essence, the telegraph and telephone are the two inventions that really made an impact in the world of telecommunications, although the telephone has eclipsed the telegraph. Can we think of a world without telephones? The answer is 'we cannot' for those who are privileged to have access to one. For most in the rural areas of the developing worlds, telephony is a luxury.

1.3 TELEPHONE NETWORK

Two telephone equipments can be connected to form a simple network, as shown in Fig. 1.7. The need to communicate with each other by a number of telephone services requires a more robust network be formulated.

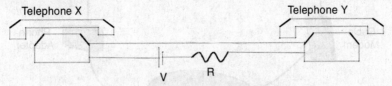

Telephone X   Telephone Y

V   R

Fig. 1.7. A simple telephone network

As seen in Fig. 1.7, it is clearly impracticable to connect a community of telephone-users together in this hybrid manner. This would require a vast number of circuits with each one only used for a small proportion of time, if at all, and some form of selection arrangement would be needed at each user's premises to connect the instrument at the required line. Regrettably, such a system would have to be continuously expanded at every point as new services were connected. As a result a well-planned, well-resourced telecommunications network would need to be visualized that groups links into nodes. In real situation, a speech-transmission network, for example, is composed of a chain of various transmission, switching and terminal equipment. The quality of such a network is influenced by the characteristics of each of the channels in the network's transmission path. More is said about Network Planning, switching, etc, from Chapter 2 onwards. Quality is always linked to the users perceived characteristics as well as to the situational context in which quality is experienced. In essence, quality is the result of a perception-cum-judgment process. More is said about *quality of service* in Chapter 3.

1.4 TELEFAX AND INTERNET INFLUENCE

The boundary between telephony and telegraphy is somehow blurred by (*i*) compactly combining telephone and facsimile devices called telefax (also called teleprinter) as in Fig. 1.8, and (*ii*) by new technology called *Internet* network facilitated by computer systems and telephony network. The disadvantage of combining facsimile and telephone is the disengagement of the other device when the other is in operation. For example, if the fax machine is enabled, the phone will be disabled: operating an Exclusive OR arrangement.

There are facilities provided by the internet like email which can deliver written documents, manage faxing by

Fig. 1.8. Telefax

automatically sending and receiving documents using existing applications, as well as voice communication using *voice over internet protocol.*

1.4.1 Voice over Internet Protocol

Voice over internet protocol (VoIP) is a technology that allows you to make voice calls using a broadband (*i.e.*, broad bandwidth) Internet connection instead of a regular (or analogue) phone line. A configuration of VoIP is shown in Fig. 1.9.

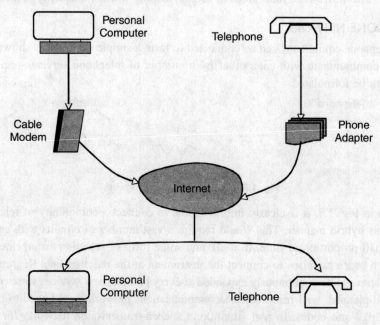

Fig. 1.9. Internet Protocol enabled services

Ideally, VoIP services would allow you to call anyone who has a telephone number—including local, long distance, mobile, and international numbers. Some VoIP services only work over your computer or a special VoIP phone, other services allow you to use a traditional phone connected to a VoIP adapter. The choice is dependent on Internet Service Provider (ISP).

1.4.1.1 *How VoIP Works*

VoIP services convert your voice (sound wave) into a digital signal that travels over the Internet. If you are calling a regular phone number, the signal is converted to a regular telephone signal before it reaches the destination. VoIP can allow you to make a call directly from a computer, a special VoIP phone, or a traditional phone connected to a special phone adapter. In addition, wireless Internet service is providing other alternative to those on the move. This is facilitated by wireless 'hot spots' in locations such as in coffee shops, hotels, airports, and more added all the time. Hot spots are functional areas that turn on an application or other functions when activated. Wireless 'hot spots' allow you to connect to the Internet and may enable you to use VoIP service wirelessly—without recourse via a modem.

A modem is an electronic device that modulates outgoing digital signals (expressed as a string of 0's and 1's) from a computer or other digital device to analogue signals (represented by a series of sine waves) for a conventional copper twisted pair telephone line and demodulates the incoming analogue signal and converts it to a digital signal for the digital device. In recent years, most new personal computers are equipped with 56,000 bits per second (56 kb/s) and higher modems: subject to signal power limitations without causing interference or other technical problems as stipulated by the ITU and relevant national regulations. With Digital Subscriber Line (DSL) systems, now being deployed in a number of communities, bandwidth on twisted-pair can be in the megabit range.

It is never useless to repeat even the obvious. Each of these 0's and 1's state digits is referred to as a *bit*, and a string of bits that a computer can address individually as a group is a *byte*. 8 bits equal 1 byte.

1.5 ANALOGUE AND DIGITAL TRANSMISSION: AN EXPLANATION

Many physical systems are characterised by processes which change continuously with time. Humans experience the world analogically. Analogue means the signals are continuous; they change smoothly from one state to another with time, like *sine* or *cosine* waves. As such, the amplitude, phase, or some other property of an analogue signal varies in a direct proportion to the instantaneous value of a physical variable. Vision, for example, is an analogue experience because we (humans) perceive infinitely smooth gradations of shapes and colours.

As a technology, analogue is the process of taking an audio or video signal (for example, the human voice) and translating it into electronic pulses. Thus, an analogue transmission uses signals that are exact replicas of a sound wave or picture being transmitted. Signals of varying frequency or amplitude are added to carrier waves with a given frequency of electromagnetic current to produce a continuous electric wave. An example of analogue transmission is the analogue telephone system where an electric current, or the reproduction of patterned sound waves, is transmitted through a wire and into the telephone receiver. Once this is completed, the transmitted signal is then converted back into sound waves.

The transmission of analogue voice signals may be attractive in small, short-haul systems especially for shorter distances, where costs can be minimized and complex multiplexing and

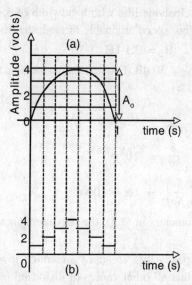

Fig. 1.10. Quantization process: (a) original analogue signal of amplitude A_o; and (b) quantized version of the signal

timing equipment may be unnecessary. Also, fibre optic sensor systems may incorporate analogue transmission. Note that most fibre-optic systems employ digital modulation techniques; there are certain applications where analogue modulation techniques are preferred. Requirements that analogue transmission places on applications include high signal-to-noise ratio and high source linearity. For long-haul systems, digital techniques provide better performance, and are preferred for long-distance transmission.

A digital system, on the other hand, quantizes or breaks signal into a prescribed number of discrete amplitude levels—like an ascending and descending staircase, as demonstrated in Fig. 1.10. To sample the original signal, and if we are to reduce quantisation error, we must sample twice the rate of the bandwidth, i.e., $2f_m$. This sampling rate is called *Nyquist* rate.

In general any one quantised signal sample may be coded into a group of m pulses, each with n possible amplitude levels. These m pulses may be transmitted in the original sampling interval allotted to the quantised sample. Since the information carried by the m pulses is equivalent to the information carried by the original s amplitude levels, the number of possible amplitude combinations of m pulses must equal s. Thus

$$s = n^m \tag{1.3}$$

For example, for binary pulses if $s = 8$, $m = 3$.

If each quantised signal carries $\log_2 s$ bits of information, the system capacity or rate of information transmission, C, must be

$$C = 2f_m \log_2 s \qquad b/s \tag{1.4}$$

Shannon (1949) showed that the maximum possible rate of transmission of binary digits with B $(= 2f_m)$ bandwidth, considering the effect of noise N in the transmission channel, could be expressed as:

$$C = B \log_2 \left(1 + \frac{S}{N}\right) \qquad b/s \tag{1.5}$$

This equation is known as the Shannon limit.

Example 1: Consider a telephone line with bandwidth of 3.1 kHz and signal-to-noise ratio of 30 dB. Calculate the signalling speed attainable through the line.

Solution: Bandwidth,   B = 3.1 kHz

Signal to noise ratio, (S/N) = 30 dB. Convert this value to actual value of the quantity being measured. Note that:

$$X_{dB} = 10 \log_{10} \left(\frac{S}{N}\right)$$

or

$$\frac{S}{N} = 10^{X_{dB}/10}$$

So,

$$\left(\frac{S}{N}\right) = 10^3 = 1000.$$

By substituting these parameters in (1.5), the maximum signalling speed attainable is about 30.9 kb/s.

In practice, signalling speeds that are used are much lower than both the Nyquist and Shannon limit. One reason is that all other causes of distortion (*e.g.*, echo, cross-talk, non-linear frequency dependent distortions, channel attenuation, etc.) are not taken into consideration in arriving at their solutions. Typical data and error rates for three common types of physical media are given in Table 1.1.

Table 1.1. Data and error rates of physical media [Holzmann, 1991]

Description	Twisted Pair	Coaxial Cable	Optical Fibre
Bandwidth, B (kHz)	250	350	1000
Bit Error Rate (BER)	10^{-5}	10^{-6}	10^{-9}
Data Rate (in Mb/s)	10	100	1000

Bit *error rate* (BER) is the ratio of the number of bit errors to the total number of bits in a digital signal transmitted in a given time interval. It is an empirical record of a system's actual bit error performance.

In essence, if the quantised signals were transmitted directly as pulses of varying heights, the resultant system could be a modified form of PAM (pulse amplitude modulation). But with discrete or numbered voltage levels, each level can be coded in some arbitrary form before transmission, as in Fig. 1.11. The reader might ask, why code? A coded system makes much more efficient use of bandwidth widening to increase the output signal-to-noise ratio than does an uncoded system.

As in Fig. 1.11(*b*), the quantized signal is coded in *binary coded decimal* (BCD) representation where each decimal digit is converted to its 4-bit pure binary equivalent. Binary means "two," or "base two." The binary system is a way of counting using just the two numbers: 0 and 1. The value of any position in a binary number increases by a power of 2 each moving from right to left {1 (2^0), 2 (2^1), 4 (2^2), 8 (2^3), 16 (2^4), 32 (2^5), ...}. For example, 1110 in the binary number system represents $(1 \times 2^3) + (1 \times 2^2) + (1 \times 2^1) + (0 \times 2^0)$, which adds up to 14 in the decimal system.

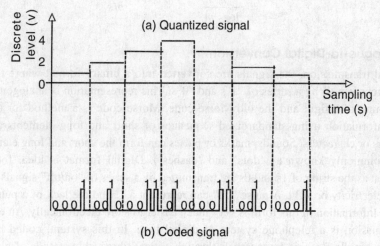

Fig. 1.11. Quantization and coding process

A system in which the standard values of a quantised wave are indicated by '1s' and '0s' coded signals is called *pulse-code modulation* (PCM) system. There are two standards of PCM systems, namely: the North American 24-channel system (T_1 carrier standard), or the European (E_1 carrier standard) or ITU equivalent 30-channel system. Although the two systems employ basically the same principles, they use different philosophies as far as signalling is concerned. More is said about the T/E- carrier standard in chapter 3, section 3.2, as well as in chapter 5 on signalling.

1.5.1 PCM Philosophical difference between the T_1 and E_1 Carrier Standards

The basic principle of a 30-channel PCM is that analogue circuits are sampled at a rate of 8 kb/s and the resulting sample is quantised and encoded into an equivalent 8-bit code. This gives an overall signalling rate of 64 kb/s, which is subsequently sampled at 2.048 Mb/s and transmitted (*i.e.*, sent to line). In practice, there are 32 channels of which 30 channels are dedicated to voice or speech; one channel is dedicated to signalling, and the remainder to housekeeping and synchronization. Whilst in the 24-channel version, only 7 bits are used for speech; thus giving a sample data rate of 56 kb/s and the remaining bit is used for line signalling. In addition, a framing or synchronization bit is added to the data stream resulting in an overall line rate of 1.544 Mb/s.

1.5.2 System Capacity

Other question the reader may ask could be: How does the coding of quantised signal enable us to improve system capacity, or make more efficient use of the increased bandwidth? The following clears up this question, thus.

Consider the transmission of a binary group as an illustration. All we have to do at the receiver is to recognise the absence or presence of a pulse, and then decode into the quantised form to reconstruct the signal. By originally transmitting binary pulses of high enough amplitude, we can ensure correct detection of the pulses in the presence of noise with as low an error rate (or possibility of mistakes) as required. For instance, if we send m binary pulses instead of 1 multilevel pulse, we require m times the bandwidth.

Note that if n bits are grouped together, then $m = 2^n$ levels are needed. As a consequence the m-ary signalling rate will change from that of the original rate. Specifically, if the original bit rate is r_b, then the m-ary signalling rate can be expressed as

$$r_{m-ary} = \frac{r_b}{\log_2 m} \qquad b/s \qquad\qquad (1.6)$$

1.5.3 Analogue-to-Digital Conversion

In digital transmission, the signals are converted into a binary format where the audio or video data is represented by a series of "1"s and "0"s. This representation is analogous to the "on and off" flashing of a light and the old Morse code. Morse code is a method for transmitting telegraphic information using standardized sequences of short and long elements to represent message letters or characters. Sounds, marks or pulses can form the short and long elements, in *on off keying* (commonly known as 'dots' and 'dashes'). Digital format is ideal for electronic communication as the string of 1s and 0s are transmitted by a series of "on/off" signals represented by pulses of electricity or light. A pulse "on" can represent a 1, and the lack of a pulse "off" can represent a 0. Information in this form is very much easier to store electronically. An example of a digital transmission is a telephone system of digital type. In this system, coded light signals produced by a rapidly flashing laser travels through optical fibres (thin strands of glass) and are then decoded by the receiver. When transmitting a telephone conversation, the light flashes on and off about 450 million times per second. This high rate enables two optical fibres to carry about 15,000 conversations simultaneously. Nanotechnology is very likely to accelerate the development of "Gigabit Networks" and to deliver improved versatility through faster data (voice, data, image and video information) transfer, more mobile processing power and larger data storage. More is said about nanotechnology in chapter 10.

In transmission of speech, audio, or video information, the object is high fidelity—that is, the best possible reproduction of the original message without the degradations imposed by signal distortion and noise. The basis of relatively noise-free and distortion-free telecommunication is the binary signal. To accomplish this goal, a device called an analogue-to-digital converter (ADC) is used to convert analogue signal to digital binary numbers ('0's, '1's). At the receiving end of the transmission, the stream of numbers is converted back to an analogue wave by a digital-to-analogue converter (DAC). The analogue wave produced by the DAC is amplified and fed to the loudspeakers to produce the expected sound, as long as the numbers are not corrupted. The analogue wave produced by the DAC will also be very similar to the original analogue wave if the analog-to-digital converter sampled at a high rate and produced accurate numbers. The *digital switch block* (DSB), in Fig 1.12, undertakes the necessary signal switching. More is said about signalling and switching in Chapters 5 and 6 respectively.

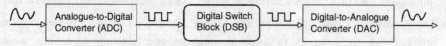

Fig. 1.12. Analogue/Digital Switching

In essence, digital transmission is usually faster and involves less noise and disturbances as compared to analogue data transmission. This permits an exactness of measurement and control impossible in analogue systems.

1.6 INTERNATIONAL TELECOMMUNICATION UNION

The International Telecommunication Union (ITU) is the leading United Nations agency for information and communication technologies within which the public and private sectors cooperate for the development of telecommunications. It must be noted that this section gains from the articles written by the ITU on their website [ITU, 2007]. ITU adopts international regulations and treaties governing all terrestrial and space uses of the frequency spectrum, within which countries adopt their national legislation. As well, it develops standards to facilitate the interconnection of telecommunication systems on a worldwide scale regardless of the type of technology used. Basically, the role of this Agency spans three core sectors: radiocommunication, standardization, and development wherein their functionalities are summarised below.

The Radiocommunication Sector (ITU-R) plays a vital role in the management of the radio-frequency spectrum and satellite orbits, finite natural resources which are increasingly in demand from a large number of services such as fixed, mobile, broadcasting, amateur, space research, meteorology, global positioning systems, environmental monitoring and, last but not least, those communication services that ensure safety of life on land, at sea, and in the skies.

The Telecommunication Standardization Sector (ITU-T[1]) forms the foundations of the information and communications technologies of today. The ITU-T is responsible for studying technical, operating and tariff questions, and issuing Recommendations on them with a view to standardizing telecommunications on a worldwide basis. Standardization facilitates the interconnection of telecommunication systems on a worldwide scale regardless of the type of technology used.

---

[1] As a result of a reform process within the ITU, the CCITT (the International Telegraph and Telephone Consultative Committee) ceased to exist as of 28 February, 1993. In its place, the ITU-T was created as of 1 March, 1993.

The World Telecommunication Standardization Conference (WTSC), which meets every four years, established the topics for study by the ITU-T Study Groups, which, in their turn, produce Recommendations on these topics. These Recommendations help drive the global information society that allows social and economic development worldwide. Anytime we make a simple telephone call, send or receive *text message*, that is, SMS (Short Message Service) messages, or receive streaming video to your mobile phone or computer, an ITU-T Recommendation will have played a fundamental role.

Industry and government members develop ITU-T Recommendations in a unique contribution-driven and consensus-based environment, with industry providing the most significant input.

Each country has an administrative arm or technical associations that oversee standards, spectrum allocation, and other technical related issues. As an illustration, to mention a few:

o The Australian Communications and Media Authority (ACMA) is the regulator for broadcasting, the Internet, radiocommunications and telecommunications, as well as licensing and spectrum allocation in Australia.

o In USA, the Telecommunications Industry Association (TIA) is accredited by the American National Standards Institute (ANSI) to develop voluntary industry standards for a wide variety of telecommunications products. TIA's Standards and Technology Department is composed of five divisions, which sponsor more than 70 standards formulating groups. The committees and subcommittees sponsored by the five divisions (Fiber optics, User Premises Equipment, Wireless Communications, Communications Research and Satellite Communications) formulate standards to serve the industry and users.

o In Nigeria, the Nigerian Communications Commission (NCC) is the regulatory authority for the telecommunications services including licensing and spectrum allocation.

The Telecommunication Development Sector (ITU-D) aims at achieving the Sector's objectives based on the right to communicate by all inhabitants of the planet through access to infrastructure and information and communication services. The Sector's mission encompasses ITU's dual responsibility as a United Nations specialized agency and an executing agency for implementing projects under the United Nations development system or other funding arrangements.

1.7 CONCLUSION

The field of telecommunication engineering is so wide: it embraces modern communications networks and systems. This chapter has attempted to introduce some of the fundamentals of relevance to the field, which would be built upon in the subsequent chapters, as well as the role that the International Telecommunication Union plays in ensuring the development and standardization of telecommunications systems. The author now embarks on a series of chapters in which the subject treatment is more detailed and focused, commencing with network planning and design.

QUESTIONS

1. Design a simple telephone. Explain how it works, including how to prevent backtalk or unpleasant ringing tone.

2. Can a non-sinusoidal signal be considered an analogue signal?

3. What type of modulation do most analogue fibre optic communications systems use?

4. Why has the transmission of video using analogue techniques been very popular, especially for shorter distances?

5. Describe the processes or stages required of an information-transmission system.

6. Describe the process required to ensure that information transfer from analogue devices to digital are faithfully transmitted.

7. A telephone channel has a bandwidth of 3.1 kHz. Experimentally, we found that the signal-to-noise ratio is 30 dB.

   (*i*) Estimate the data rate for error-free communication.

   (*ii*) Compare the above result with a 28.8 kbaud modem. What do you conclude?

   (*iii*) Explain what a modem is.

   (*iv*) How then is it possible to have a 56 kbaud modem?

   (*v*) Describe how a connection is established between your computer at home and the university main terminal.

8. If a binary message 10110100 is received, what is the numeral conveyed?

2

NETWORK PLANNING AND DESIGN

A public telephone network allows for multiple connections between diverse communications devices and more importantly between end users. Typically, a network consists of various routing points in local switching stations and an extended network of end-user-terminal devices. Figure 2.1 shows a modern, inter-related communications network.

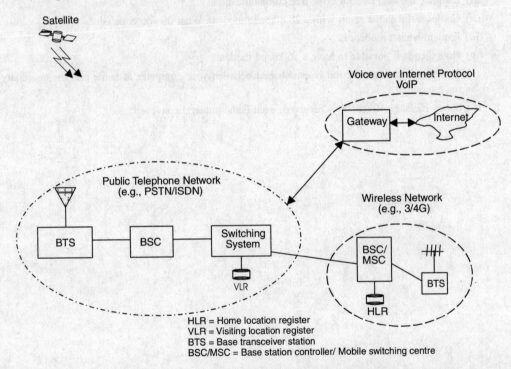

Fig. 2.1. An architecture of Communications Networks

Advances in technology have accelerated the establishment of different access networks envisioned to be equipped with multiple interfaces to establish connections with different types of landline and wireless access networks. Consequently, a network designer must take into account end-users' needs, systems protocols, information (data, voice, etc) security, and physical equipment requirements; such as, proper subscribers lines, wiring and routing or switching devices, as well as network-site acquisition and buildings that house the local sub-networks. This suggests that there is a need for proper planning and design so that a balance may be struck between various components of the networks that gives maximum total network economy as well as meeting customers and technical demands and standards.

The networks-classification in Fig. 2.1 forms the central theme of this book. Each network and related components are treated under associated topics and headings. The concept of 'voice over internet protocol (VoIP)' network has been described in Chapter 1, section 1.4.1. Communications satellite and mobile (or wireless) network are discussed respectively in chapters 7 and 8. This chapter (*i.e.*, chapter 2) through to chapter 6 will concentrate on public telephone network since it forms the backbone of subsequent networks.

2.1 NETWORK PRIMARY CONSIDERATIONS

Generally, telecommunications network plans and designs are presented by four basic plans, namely:

(a) Switching plans—showing the network hierarchy, the switching rules that must be followed, and the areas that would be served by each switching stage.

(b) Transmission plans—giving the overall loss, and specifying the way the loss is to be distributed throughout the network. It shows the loss in and out of each switching stage in the network. Standards for stability, echo, and sometimes-extraneous noise are included. Depending on the system and the organisation building the network, details of signalling scheme may be included in the standards or specifications. Other organisations may opt to have signalling scheme as a separate plan.

(c) Numbering plans—containing the numbering rules, area codes, area code boundaries, and exchange prefixes within those boundaries.

(d) Charging plans—showing the charging principles adopted, and the area boundaries and groupings where applicable.

These plans can be used for the development of most aspects of the trunk network either for a particular section of a network, for a network of a geographic area, or for a national network configuration. How these plans pan out would depend on several factors, which are discussed next.

2.2 FACTORS THAT INFLUENCE THE PLANNING AND DESIGN OF A TELECOMMUNICATIONS NETWORK

As an engineer or a scientist, it is intuitive to identify the factors that will influence the planning and design of a telecommunications network. The major factors can be narrowed down to the following:

(i) Community needs and expectation-including benefits, security of systems and users information, satisfaction, access to network or transferring of service from one location to another, and affordable service-delivery cost.

(ii) Network performance standards-ensuring that the network provides good quality of service as required by customers/users. These dictates require certain technical specifications to be considered including:

   o Transmission standards;

   o Grade of service;

   o Numbering-accommodating interconnect requirements;

   o Signalling;

   o Survivability.

These technical specifications or standards should attempt to ensure that the users of the network receive quality service without going beyond the bounds of economic realism. The standards must also comply with international standards recommended by the Telecommunication Standardization Sector (ITU-T) of the International Telecommunications Union (ITU) ensuring that international telephone communication is not impeded.

(*iii*) Economic considerations;

(*iv*) Organisational structure and Compliances-including

o International standards;

o Existing network structure;

o Administration needs;

o Future considerations and flexibility.

Each of these major factors is discussed under appropriate headings later in this chapter, as well as in subsequent chapters where appropriate.

2.3 COMMUNITY NEEDS AND EXPECTATION

The primary purpose of building a telecommunication network is to contribute to the communications needs of the community for social, business, and government purposes. To meet these needs a telephone system is required that is simple to use, reliable and secure (*i.e.*, free from interference associated with noise or distortion, cross-talks, etc). Users of the telephone system expect to reach any other service, local, national or international, at any time and in any situation. There should be no impediment to gaining connection to the network or transferring a service from one location to another.

The telephone network must be capable of looking ahead in terms of development of communications facilities which the community of users will require in the future in addition to supporting and meeting the current needs.

Community characteristics that have a major effect on the network structure are population density and distribution, the degree of the sophistication of the economy, the standard of living, the general cultural level, and the availability, cost, and effectiveness of alternative means of communication.

The need to provide high quality of service and the need to limit the cost of delivery of service places an obligation on the network designer to make optimum use of the resources.

The choice of what service to provide depends on the capability of the network providing the telecommunication services. In the era of space communications, the service provider has the choice of terrestrial and satellite technologies, and may be able to select the most appropriate solution to satisfy customer requirements including a combination of satellite and terrestrial systems. The principle of communications satellite is discussed in chapter 7.

In some instances satellite transmission represents the only viable option of voice or data services. Examples of where this mode can be deployed include operations in inhospitable terrain, remote areas, transportable voice and data services (also called *mobile ad-hoc network*, MANET), 'special events' such as in natural disaster zones like tsunami, earthquakes, or battle zones, and for maritime operations. The provision of satellite services should be a part of the charter of community service obligations.

2.4   NETWORK PERFORMANCE STANDARDS

In compliance with international standards set by the ITU-T, certain technical standards must be specified that ensure the users of the telephone network receive a satisfactory quality of service without going beyond the bounds of economic reality. These include:

o Transmission standards

o Grade of service

o Numbering-accommodating interconnect requirements

o Signalling

o Survivability.

Each of these performance standards is elaborated on under appropriate headings in this section, and specified wherever appropriate in other sections of this book.

2.4.1   Transmission Standards

The transmission standards chosen will usually indicate the maximum power loss that will be permitted in the network, and will allocate acceptable loss-values through various sections of the network. Other parameters that are specified include bandwidth, noise, echo, and crosstalk.

Establishing transmission standards is a complex problem since the objective is to specify the quality of communication from one subscriber (speaker) to another subscriber (listener), which involves an essentially subjective judgment because such standards will be affected by several factors other than network and telephone instrument itself. Background room noise, the user's standard of hearing and speech, as well as the method by which the telephone instrument is used have a significant effect on the quality of a conversation. Despite the difficulties, transmission standards are necessary as they determine the quality of much of the plant provided in the network with the obvious relationship to cost.

In settling overall transmission standards, the network must be designed so that as many calls as possible experience the standard. As such, in selecting the transmission standards to be adopted, network architects and administrations should comply with the standards required for international traffic since every service in the network is a potential participant in an international call. This implies that relevant ITU-T Recommendations on transmission standards should be taken into account when settling overall network transmission standards and follow the guidance given in the Recommendations. Of course, nothing stops national network operators improving on the Recommendations; they serve as minimum acceptable standards.

Once the overall standard is determined it is necessary to allocate it throughout the various sections of the network. The main factors that affect this distribution are:

o Subscribers lines, though numerous, are relatively short and very lightly loaded by traffic.

o Long distance inter-exchange circuits are amplified, have low loss, and are relatively few.

o Other inter-exchange circuits, and other accessories such as junctions, are relatively numerous. These junctions are probably costlier than subscriber lines and shorter than trunk circuits, and used efficiently.

o Wherever possible, calls should not experience a standard of transmission in which wide variations occur.

While the distribution of transmission loss throughout the network may be dictated by economic considerations, it is important that the overall standard and its distribution are specified in a way that lends support to accurate measurement so that the actual transmission performance of network can be measured and compared with the set standard.

The way the loss is distributed in various sections of a network is discussed in Chapter 3, section 3.5.

2.4.2 Grade of Service Standards

Selection of the 'grade of service' standard is primarily based on a subjective assessment of the standard of service the network's users will regard as satisfactory. This is difficult to determine.

Call congestion due to delay, and the duration of that delay, is one way of measuring customers satisfaction.

The overall congestion (or loss) grade of service of a network is the probability that a connection cannot be made between a calling and called party. This loss may be related to insufficient provision of network plant, network failing to operate properly due to minor overload conditions, the called party using the service, or due to natural disaster, etc. When planning, a nominally achievable standard must be set as overall standard, which is then distributed over various components of the network. At any particular point, an analysis of the network can be performed to measure against the benchmark.

The congestion (or blocking) grade of service is usually expressed as a ratio or a decimal number. This may, for instance, be one lost call in 100, or 0.01-normally refers to as the loss, which may be designed to occur during the period of maximum traffic flow. In the USA, most state and federal public utility commissions hold public switched telephone network (PSTN) operating companies to requirements for blocking on less than 1% of call attempts (colloquially called P01). In practice, most wire PSTN operators achieve less than 0.1% (P001). Cellular and personal communications systems strive for 2% blocking (P02) and sometimes are temporarily at P05 in some problem areas, due to lack of sufficient radio traffic channels.

In addition, delay grade of service is another parameter that can be considered. Delay includes:

o The pre-dial delay: the time a caller must wait before receiving a dial tone.

o The post dialling delay: the time that elapses between completion of dialling and completion of the connection.

o The delay calls experience in queues.

In telecommunication engineering, the quality of voice service is specified by two measures: the grade of service (GoS) and the quality of service (QoS). As noted in chapter 1 Section 1.3, quality is always linked to the users perceived characteristics as well as to the situational context in which quality is experienced because, in practice, a speech-transmission network may be a chain of transmission, switching and terminal equipment. The quality of service of such a network is influenced by the characteristics of each of the channels in the network's transmission path. These quantifiable measures (*i.e.*, GoS and QoS) are explored further in Chapters 3 and 9.

2.5 NETWORK NUMBERING PLAN

A network-numbering plan must aim to give each service a unique identity that would enable each service to be called by any other service in the network, or from international callers. Importantly, the numbering scheme should be easy to understand and use; it should avoid the need for dialling large number of digits; and it should comply with international standards for the maximum numbers of digits.

The international telecommunication union—standardization sector, ITU-T, via Recommendation [U.7] is of the view that:

(*a*) National numbering plans should be systematically arranged.

(*b*) Where more than one international trunk route exist between two countries, the corresponding geographical division and hence the appropriate point of entry should be identifiable by examination of the initial digits of the called subscriber's national number.

(*c*) Where a multiple tariff scale exists, the different tariff zones should be identifiable in the originating country by the initial digits of the called subscriber's national number.

(*d*) The number of initial digits of the subscriber's national number to be examined for routing purposes should be limited, to one, but in any case should not exceed two. When a single digit provides the discrimination it will usually be the first digit, but, where the subscribers' national numbers have a uniform initial digit (usually 0) to permit discrimination on national calls, the following (second) digit should be used.

(*e*) The national telex numbering plan should be arranged in such a way that the destination code and the national number does not exceed 12 digits in accordance with Recommendation U.11.

ITU-T sets out the *International Direct Dialling* (IDD) codes for each country [E.164]. As seen in Fig. 2.2, for example, the IDD codes for North America, Australia, India and Nigeria are 1, 61, 91 and 234 respectively. The country code is the *national prefix* to be used when dialing to that particular country *from* another country.

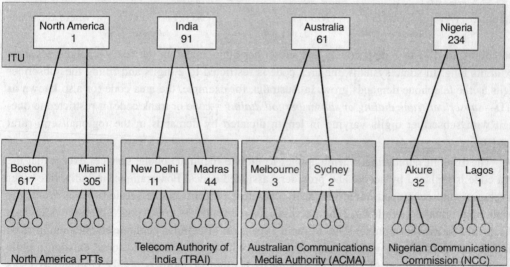

Fig. 2.2. Numbering the Networks and the responsible authorities

Each country decides how to run their local numbering system. Each country has a designated authority that administers and oversees the numbering systems among other functions as described by the Act (of Parliament) that sets it up. North America PTT, Australian Communications Media Authority, Telecom Authority of India and Nigerian Communications Commission are the responsible authorities respectively for USA, Australia, India and Nigeria.

2.5.1   National Numbering Scheme

A national-network-numbering scheme should serve areas of community interest. The desirability of providing special simple and universal codes for access to special services and for trunk access, and the need to avoid frequent changes to customers should form the basis for allotting subscribers numbers. Geography plays an important role in the planning phase, as well as telephone density and economics including future population of service users. This consideration would guide on how to distribute numbers.

A national numbering plan always contains a feature code, N (such as *access code* digit '0', and level '1' for *special services*) preceding the area code and each subscriber unique number. Most countries have a maximum of 9 numerical digits, designated ABCDEFGHI. This gives a theoretical capacity of more than 100 million numbers. In emerging economies, like Nigeria and Brazil, the numbering plan may have 8 numerical digits, designated ABCDEFGH, as a maximum. The area code may vary in length, depending on the length used in the closed area being accessed. With the area code, the length of the national number including the feature code, N, could be as long as 10 digits. What A and other alphabets, in the designate, stand for become obvious as we plough through this section.

2.5.1.1   *Allocation of Area Codes*

The A digit is allotted for the *area code*. State, regional or provincial boundaries may be used to allot the area code, but this may not be strictly true. Regions or cities with low population may have longer area codes, while centres with dense population may have shorter area codes. In order to maintain numbering consistency, say, a 10-digit number scheme may be commissioned. For

example, $\underset{\text{subscriber-number}}{(\overset{\text{area-code}}{N}x) \quad xxxxxxxx}$, $\underset{\text{subscriber-number}}{(\overset{\text{area-code}}{N}xx) \quad xxxxxxx}$, $\underset{\text{subscriber-number}}{(\overset{\text{area-code}}{N}xxx) \quad xxxxxx}$ where the area-

code digits are 1, 2 or 3 respectively and subscriber digits make up the rest; *i.e.*, eight, seven or six digits long. In some systems, the area code is restricted to 2 digits and filling the subscriber digits as the telephone demands grow. In Australia, for example, the area code (or also known as STD—*subscriber trunk dialing or subscriber toll dialing*—code or trunk code) is restricted to one-digit with subscriber digits varying in length dictated by demands in the regional/semi-rural districts.

The 10-digit numbering scheme applies to mobile (cellular) phone services except that the area code is replaced by access and providers' assigned codes. For example, in India, like other developing and developed countries, many operators perform phone services. As a result, the numbering format is as follows: 2-digit access code (currently 98 or 94) plus 3-digit provider code plus 5-digit subscriber number. Due to rapid expansion of cellular phone users, beginning from 2009 the 10-digit format will increase to 11-digit with 9 being prefixed to all existing mobile numbers. The likelihood of China increasing to 11-digit or more is highly probable as users become larger in number.

The number format in the North America has the same 10-digit national numbers but use larger area codes to accommodate the large number of countries (from American Samoa and including the Caribbean nations to United States) comprising the North American Numbering Plan (NANP). The number format is (Nxx) xxxxxxx: 3-digit area codes followed by 7-digit local numbers.

In the ABCDEFGH format for Nigeria, it allots a 2-digit maximum length for area codes and 7-digit maximum for subscriber number accommodating for future expansion, *i.e.*, (*Nxx*) *xxxxxxx*. For example, most geographic areas with the exception of the major population centres like Lagos, Ibadan, etc, have 2-digit area code and 6-digit local numbers. The major population centres or designated geographic centres like Lagos, Ibadan, etc have 1-digit area code and 7-digit local numbers plus [1] reserved for future demands.

2.5.1.2 *Rationale for Other Digits Assignment*

Within a State, region or province, the B digit is allotted to areas with high community of interest. This generally comprises the number of switching area, which often coincides with a single secondary switching area. Generally, 0AB codes are allotted to secondary networks. However, for convenience of telephone charging and routing purposes, a 0AB code may be allotted to a large minor switching network.

The distribution of the 0ABC codes is of considerable importance in the automatic charging of calls as analysis of the initial digits of the national number determines the correct charge for the call. Automatic charging equipment will examine the national number as far as the C digit to ascertain the charge for long distance calls, or to determine whether further digits need be examined to provide more precise charging on the shorter distance calls where analysis to the D or E digit may be required. More is said about charging plan in the Section 2.7.

Since the advent of mobile number portability, numbering scheme remains the same 10-digit number, but a particular number is allotted to the A digit for all wireless-network providers in each country. The differentiator is the B or C digit. Note that there is no area code assigned to mobile numbering plan. Of course the access code is still present except if the calling party is from another country. There may be a fixed relationship between the mobile phone number and the network it

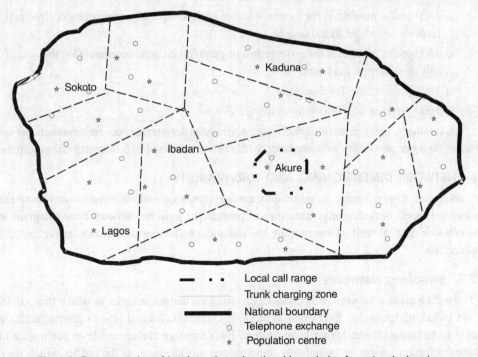

       ▬ **·** ·   Local call range
       ·············   Trunk charging zone
       ▬▬▬▬   National boundary
       ○   Telephone exchange
       ☆   Population centre

Fig. 2.3. Representation of local, trunk, and national boundaries for network charging

uses depending on the country's numbering policies. However, for fixed line telephones, the 0 followed by the single digit area code does not need to be dialled when calling locally, *i.e.*, local call range (see Fig. 2.3).

The access code is used when making trunk calls *within* the country: trunk calls could be from one city to another-when calling another city in the same local call range, this may not be necessary. When making trunk calls within the same country, the access code is followed by the area code of the subscriber's place you are calling and then the subscriber's number.

Numbers allocated within an area code X can be replicated in another area, say area code Y. Obviously, the separation distance between 'user A' assigned same number in area X must be sufficiently large to prevent interference to device of 'user B' of same number in area Y. For A to communicate with 'user B', A has to include the area code to reach the intended user. If user A has a mobile phone and keys in his land number and travels to zone Y and attempts to call home without his/her area-code prefixed to home number, user B will receive the call instead.

2.5.1.3 *Special Services Codes*

Every nation develops policies that mandate the telecommunications providers to provide subscribers access codes to special services. A range of service codes adopted for use are short and easily remembered codes for more important services such as Emergency, for example: in Australia '000' for fire, accident or ambulance; while in Nigeria, '115', '118' and '119' numbers are used for national emergency, ambulance and fire services respectively. The internationally recognised GSM (*global system for mobile*) mobile emergency telephone number is 112, which works for mobile telephones.

Other special services' numbering scheme varies for different activities from country to country. For example, in Australia the

- o 1800 prefix number is for natural disaster or other special announcement (free call from landline anywhere in the country).
- o 1300 prefix number is for government or commercial announcement (for the cost of local call anywhere in the country).
- o 1400 prefixes are for Satellite
- o 1600 prefixes are for paging system, etc.

In summary, any numbering plans must accommodate interconnect requirements, as well as ensuring number portability in accordance with relevant national and international requirements.

2.6 NETWORK DIMENSIONING AND SURVIVABILITY

Network dimensioning is more of capacity dimensioning: it requires developments of verifiable process of determining quantities of plant in the switched network from the given traffic and network data, as well as determining the statistical behaviour of network throughput in large populations.

2.6.1 Switching Networks

To dimension a network, it is necessary to treat exchanges in order in which they are placed in the switching hierarchy. Exchanges at the lowest level is handled first to determine the traffic that is to be passed to the higher level centres. Exchanges on the second level are handled next. These exchanges cannot be completely dimensioned at this stage, as the traffic, which they will receive from the third and higher-level centres, is not yet determined. The exchanges can only be partially dimensioned to enable dimensioning the traffic to be passed to higher level in the hierarchy, as well as the traffic to be handled at this level. Dimensioning of routes to exchanges at the lower level of the hierarchy is not complete until all higher order exchanges have been fully dimensioned. More is said about *routing* in chapter 4.

The next order exchanges must be similarly dimensioned, and the process will continue until the top exchanges in the hierarchy are completed. Fig 2.4 illustrates this principle of dimensioning. Dimensioning exchanges at level 1 determines links 1A—1B, 1A—2B, 1A—2B. Dimensioning exchanges at level 2 determines links 2A—2B, 2A—3B, 2A—3B. However, 2B—1B cannot be dimensioned until the traffic on 3B—2B is known, which in this case requires level 3 to be dimensioned.

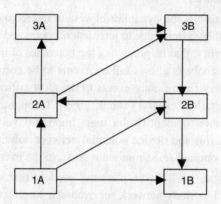

Fig. 2.4. Dimensioning exchanges

In practice, network dimensioning is typically confined to a particular section or sections of the network, and the remainder treated as single bulk sources or destinations.

2.6.2 Mathematical Modelling

All telephone network-dimensioning procedures are based on mathematical models that approximate statistical patterns that may have been experimentally observed aggregate traffic flows in real telephone networks. Traditional public switched network (*e.g.*, PSTN) utilised statistical analyses (Erlang B and C traffic models) to characterise traffic demand and network dimensioning. This approach assumes:

o Stationary traffic process during the reference period;

o Poissonian arrival of call attempts;

o General distribution of call holding times;

o Blocked calls cleared;

o Independence of call attempts and holding times on network state and other call attempts.

Assumptions are not actual descriptions of individual caller behaviour. A traffic model is fully treated in chapter 9.

2.6.3 Survivability

Survivability is a measure of the extent a network demands can be satisfied even under the risk of link or node disruption. The goal of survivability is to maintain continuous service performance to users despite underlying system failures. This should not be construed as service reliability. Reliability assumes that failures may be eliminated, while survivability assumes failures will continue to occur but mission functionality can be maintained despite underlying system degradation. In short, survivability can be considered as the appropriate risk-avoidance approach given an unbounded failure set and the potential a failure could occur which causes a large-scale outage to a critical national infrastructure if no recovery procedures exist.

The means of providing survivability can be grouped under two broad headings: preventative survivability (comprising route diversity and demand protection) and reactive survivability. Preventive survivability hopes to minimise the vulnerability of service demand in its working path assignments to the potential failure. Reactive survivability puts into action to address demand that would otherwise be lost to failure.

A network model that exhibits the dynamics of system interconnectivity, where a failure in one system can affect many other systems due to interdependencies and multiplier effects, provides a way of quantifying survivability; that is, predicting the outcomes of network survivability at any given scenario. Survivability analysis allows failure events to be correlated (as in an intelligent attack) and emphasises recovery from failure events to the most critical system components (not necessarily the most probable failure events) [Yurcik, 1999]. Through modelling and analysis, the network planner would be able to identify the most important vector component or mix of components (as decision criteria) and device potential network solutions to control the level of survivability offered in some optimal (e.g., minimum cost), in the event of system failures.

Computational, stochastic, multi-layer planning models that embrace demand forecast uncertainty are examples used to study network survivability. Results from modelling studies are generally used to determine network areas that are susceptible to malicious or intelligent attack, which are then tested on the real network.

In practice the main measures adopted to improve survivability in switched networks are:

o Diversity: using geographically separated transmission routes, different types of transmission system; and diversified allocation of circuits within a traffic route, and establishing separate switching centres where traffic volumes permit [Bennett, 1978].

o Alternative route of traffic; bearing in mind the need to guard against network overload.

o Service restoration techniques facilitated by use of spare transmission capacity where patching is possible; by use of protection bearers, by provision of transportable emergency equipment, and by use of network management techniques to control traffic flow.

o An integrated approach must be in place to detect anomaly and react to network malicious threats.

2.7 ECONOMIC CONSIDERATIONS

Telephone network plant is costly, is designed to be highly reliable, and has in economic terms virtually no resale value compared to its cost. In making decisions on investment it is important to give proper consideration to the operating and maintenance costs of the network's supporting plants over their life, as well as the initial cost of provision. It is thus necessary to have a soundly based and consistent method of evaluating the various alternatives, which can be used to develop the network. In comparing alternative schemes for network development it is necessary to analyse and compare costs over a fairly long period of time. A straight forward analysis of the cash outflow is important to disclose the requirements for capital at particular times, as well as allowing for any changes that arise thereof. As an illustration, consider the sum invested X (in any currency) at interest rate r per annum. After n years, the invested amount I_n will amount to

$$I_n = X(1 + r)^n \qquad (2.1)$$

Similarly, the present value P_v of future amount of money F_a will be

$$P_v = \frac{F_a}{(1 + r)^n} \qquad (2.2)$$

at a discount rate of r over n years. The terms: interest rate and discount rate, tend to be interchangeable, however discount rate is more appropriate.

An understanding of the investment cost and running cost allows the network administration to estimate the unit charge of the services the subscribers use.

2.7.1 Charging Plan

Charging plan is strictly a commercial decision; a service provider's prerogative, and varies from one country to another. Market forces dictate how high charges can be levelled, and also, service providers are cognizant of competition rules and the need for their business to be solvent. The bottom-line is to ensure business survival. From this basis, there are certain fundamentals that provide a clue to how charging plan evolves.

2.7.1.1 *Tariff Structure*

The measured service rate system forms the basis of the telephone tariff structure in Australia. For example, for fixed-lines telephone services, each subscriber is charged a monthly rental fee for his/her telephone service and is required to pay the prescribed local call and/or trunk fee for every effective chargeable call made from his/her telephone service. A connection fee is required for connection of a new service.

2.7.1.2 *Group Charging*

Exchanges are grouped to form zones: an example is seen in Fig. 2.5. Exchanges in any one group have a common charging basis. Charging equipment need therefore only discriminate on sufficient digits to identify the called group of exchanges, not the individual exchange.

The basis of group charging plan is described as follows.

(*i*) *Local fee charging*: Exchanges are grouped to form zones. Calls within a zone and to adjacent zones are treated as local calls. Unlike most countries, including UK, local calls in Australia are untimed and are charged at a flat rate of 1 unit fee per call.

(*ii*) *Trunk charges*: Charges are on zone basis. Zones are grouped to form districts, provinces or regions. Calls (other than local fee calls) within a district and to adjacent districts are charged at trunk rates based on three factors: the distance between zone or district centres, the time at which the call is made, and the duration of the call.

In fairness, trunk fee charging is based on range of distance between zone or district centres in which there is a corresponding charge step. Distances may be classed into kilometre-ranges: for example, 15 km to 35 km, 35 km to 55 km, 55 km to 85 km, 85 km to 165 km, etc. Each step may not be uniformly spaced. Each step has a corresponding charge scale. The combination of charge step and charge scale results in a charge rate.

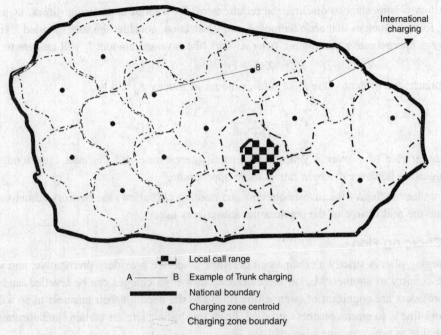

Local call range
A ——————— B   Example of Trunk charging
                     National boundary
            •   Charging zone centroid
                     Charging zone boundary

Fig. 2.5. Call charging concept

With group charging, the emphasis is on groups of exchanges rather than on geographical areas and no fixed boundary lines are intended to define the extent of charging groups.

The next question the reader may wish to ask is: how is the call duration measured and appropriate charges allotted? The next subsection sheds some light.

2.7.1.3 *Call Metering and Numbering Implications of the Charging Scheme*

Most call recorders use *periodic pulse metering* principle in which the meter registers 1 unit at a time at regular intervals during the progress of the call. The intervals between meter registrations vary with the charging rates applicable to the particular calls (*e.g.*, local or trunk fee charges). Metering equipment may be located at centres of minor switching status or higher, or may be centralised at major switching centres.

The calling subscriber's meter operates once, following answer and tone, and then at regular intervals, for each effective chargeable call. The regular interval T is the nominal period between the subscriber meter's pulse following answer and the next pulse. The charging equipment determines the rate charge to be applied to a call by using the charging zone in which the call originated, together with the digits in the number dialled by the calling subscriber (which determines the called zone or district) and the day and time (charge scale), to select the appropriate charge rate. The charge to the subscriber, y_s, has a linear time-cost relationship; that is,

$$ys \ = \ \beta + x \sum_i T_i \tag{2.3}$$

where x = the service unit cost. In the case of step charges for in-between zone or district centres situation, x still represents the corresponding charge step.

β = the rental cost (if in household) or flagfall or connection charge (if using public pay phone) and

i = the number of registered units

Charging rates on mobile phones y_m, have a subtle difference to that of landlines with a similar linear time-cost relationship like (2.3). Mobile phones' charge rates vary; dependent on the service provider and the calling country. Calls from mobile telephone are charged at a timed rate; that is, on a flagfall-plus-unit-cost basis. A standard voice call, or data rate, at all times is set at x per γ-second time block or part of, regardless of where you call within the country plus a flagfall or connection fee, β_m. For example,

$$y_m = \beta_m + x \sum_j y_j \qquad (2.4)$$

where j is the number of second-blocks registered.

There are variations in international calls rates; however, charges are still set per γ-second time block or part of, plus a call connection fee.

To permit a commercial offering of *primary rate access*, dedicated nodes are established. This primary rate access offering enables network providers to charge certain calls at premium rate. Subscribers receiving premium charges have special telephone numbers, designated like 190*xxxxxx* as in Australia irrespective of area codes. Charges are premium because they are charged higher fees than the normal even though the calls are routed the same way as the normal calls. Subscribers with these designated numbers provide certain services. Unlike a normal call, part of the call charge is paid to the service provider, thus enabling businesses to be funded via the calls.

2.7.1.3.1 *Numbering Implications of the charging Scheme*

The charging plan is coordinated with the numbering plan. Using the numerical digits ABCDEFGH, the extent of the digit examination required to determine charge rates is as follows:

o For calls within the numbering plan area – not further than the E digit;

o For calls beyond the numbering plan area but within the charging zone or district or adjacent charging zones – not further than the E digit;

o For calls beyond adjacent charging zones – generally not further than the C digit; analysis to the D digit may be required in some instances.

2.8 SUMMARY

Modern telecommunication network has become a combination of traditional switched networks, wireless networks, and voice over Internet protocol (VoIP) networks with voice communication traversing through varieties of bearer networks. This chapter has discussed some network planning and design issues, aspects of telecommunication network including trunk dimensioning, survivability, numbering plan, as well as economic considerations and commercial aspects—such as charging, metering, and tariff structure. Due to a high demand for reliable communications and power network systems, it is crucial to develop a highly survivable network that can sustain catastrophic events.

QUESTIONS

1. A Café-Internet Company leases a dedicated T1 line for $200 a day. An untimed dialup line costs 30′. Calculate how many subscribers are required to breakeven each day? Does the company need to time internet users if it were to make a profit? If so, explain a pricing structure.

2. Two sites of a company have to exchange data at an average rate of 1.8 Mb/s. Calculate the minimum number of dialup telephone lines that would be needed to carry this load, if each line can carry 30 kb/s.

3. As an engineer, you are commissioned to conduct a feasibility study to construct alternative network structures. Explain what you would consider to form planning decisions.

4. Are performance standards a mathematical exercise or consumer expectation?

5. Explain the principle of number analysis in a telephone exchange.

6. What does dimensioning the network mean?

3

PUBLIC TELEPHONE
NETWORK PRINCIPLES

This chapter attempts to identify and describe the principles that govern the structure and development of public telephone networks, particularly the way in which various components interact. Knowledge of the reasons why networks develop into the forms they do will provide a basis for deeper understanding of the existing network, and will enable students and graduate engineers and practitioners to understand and contribute to future network development.

3.1 TELECOMMUNICATION NETWORK: WHAT IS IT?

A telecommunication network can be described as a network of transmission links comprising a number of nodes (switching centres) interconnected by circuit groups (engineering routes), as shown in Fig. 3.1. In this instance, all nodes are of equal status.

In a network, as in Fig. 3.1, there may be several direct circuit groups between a pair of nodes, which may be unidirectional or bothway. As an illustration, links between node A and node C, node A and node D, are unidirectional circuit groups. While links between nodes A and B, and nodes B and C are bothway circuit groups. Calls in bothway circuit groups would share the same set of circuits, which will lead to a better efficiency especially in cases of non-coincident busy hours. In bothway operation it is necessary to take steps to protect traffic in one direction from abnormal behavior of the traffic in the other direction.

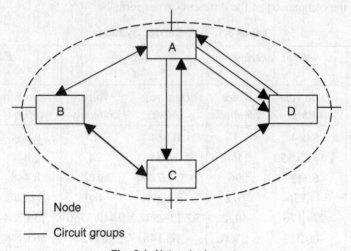

□ Node

—— Circuit groups

Fig. 3.1. Network elements

A direct route consists of one or more circuit groups connecting adjacent nodes. For example, node A communicating with node C, or node C communicating with node D, etc. An indirect route is a series of circuit groups connecting two nodes providing an end-to-end connection via other nodes. For example, directing signal from node A through node B to reach node C. In a telecommunication network, a node can be situated in a specific location and may contain one or more network elements performing network related functions. A node can be administered as a single entity. More is said about a node structure in Section 3.4.

A transmission link (or line) is a means by which telecommunication services communicate with one another. The signal or digital transmission link between two points may comprise a line section (*e.g.*, symmetric copper pairs, optical fibre, etc), or a number of line sections connected in tandem-arranged one behind another. A line section may include line terminating equipment but not multiplexers. Links, or parts thereof, can be connected together at the nodes directly or through switching systems to provide a range of communication services including TV relays, broadcasting lines, and leased lines-a transmission facility or line that is leased by an end user from a public network carrier, and which is dedicated to that user's traffic. Leased lines are always active and of specific speeds. Leased lines can be used for telephone, data or internet services; *e.g.*, E_1/T_1 lines for businesses connecting to the internet and for internet service providers (ISPs) connecting to the internet backbone (*e.g.*, T_3 connections). Some leased lines are used for ringdown services. A ringdown service is a self-locking relay that alerts a drop; when the telephone at one end goes off-hook, the phone at the other end instantly rings. Some leased lines can also be used to connect two or more telephone exchanges, *e.g.*, PBXs (or PABXs).

3.2 T-CARRIER FORMAT

T-Carrier is the generic designation for digitally multiplexed carrier classification, devised initially to transmit digitised voice signals but current applications include digital data transmission. The T preceding the 'carrier' stands for trunk, and the numeric following the 'T' represents the signal level hierarchy. However, if 'F' is appended after "T" before the numeric, it will make an optical fiber cable system at the same data rate or speed. T-carrier format is widely used in the USA, Australia and Japan, while the E-carrier system is used in Europe and UK. Table 3.1 shows the comparison of the different carrier-formats.

Table 3.1. T-/E-Carrier Systems

Signal level, DS	North America T-		Japan J-		Europe E-	
	Data rate (Mb/s)	Voice channels	Data rate (Mb/s)	Voice channels	Data rate (Mb/s)	Voice channels
0	0.064	1	0.064	1	0.064	1
1	1.544/3.152	24/48	1.544	24	2.048	32
2	6.312	96	6.312/7.786	96/120	8.448	128
3	44.736	672	32.064	480	34.368	512
4	274.176	4032	97.728/397.2	1440/5760	139.264	2048
5	400.352	5760	565.148	8192	565.148	8192

The basic digital circuit in the *public switched telephone network*, PSTN—called Digital Signal 0 (at level hierarchy '0', at times designated as DS0)—is a 64 kb/s channel, which is the basic granularity at which switching takes place in a telephone exchange. DS0s are also known as timeslots because they are multiplexed together using time-division-multiplexing (TDM) technique. E_2 (T_2, J_2) through E_5 (T_5, J_5) are carriers in increasing multiples of the E_1 (T_1, J_1) format. The T_1 carrier can operate at 1.544 Mb/s (or 3.152 Mb/s) and provide 24 (48) 64 kb/s channels. On the other hand, the E_1 carrier operates at 2.048 Mb/s and provides 32 64 kb/s channels.

There are several multiplexing techniques used in digital transmission including FDM (frequency division multiplexing), PCM[1] (pulse code modulation) multiplexing and TDM (Time Division Multiplexing). These multiplexing techniques are methods of transmitting multiple data signals simultaneously over a single wire by using multiple carriers, each having a unique centre frequency. Each data stream (text, voice, video, etc.) is placed into a separate carrier that is modulated by various methods. The principle of modulation has been discussed in Chapter 1, Section 1.2.1.1. Modern telephone systems employ digital transmission where TDM is utilised instead of FDM. In the TDM, signals are successively sampled, sent through the channel, and reconstructed at the end. In the FDM, signals are impressed on carriers of different frequencies.

This chapter concentrates on the public telephone network, but the general principles are applicable to any switched network.

Public telephone network is the generic term for public switched telephone network (PSTN); often referred to as 'fixedline'. PSTN is the standard home telephone service, delivered over copper wires. PSTN is the largest and most widespread communications network in the world, designed primarily for voice traffic-analogue, which is in contrast to newer telephone networks based on digital technologies, such as Integrated Services Digital Network (ISDN) or token-passing Fibre Distributed Data Interface (FDDI) network. Colloquially, telephone service carried by the PSTN is often called plain old telephone service (POTS). With the ISDN, the same digital switches and digital paths are used to establish connections for different services, *e.g.*, telephony, data. More is said about types of switching in chapter 6.

The PSTN is a *circuit-switched* network where a dedicated circuit (also called a channel) is established for the duration of a transmission, such as a telephone call. This contrasts with packet switching networks, in which messages are divided into small segments called packets and each packet is sent individually. An example of a packet-switching network is the Internet, where individual packets may travel different routes in compliance with certain protocol—an agreed format, for example, the Transmission Control Protocol/Internet Protocol, TCP/IP. TCP/IP is the basic communication language or protocol of the Internet, which can also be used as a communications protocol in a private network either an intranet—contained within an organization containing a number of interlinked local area networks (LANs) and using leased lines in the wide area network (WAN), or an extranet-a part of the organization's intranet extended to outside users or customers.

3.3 TELECOMMUNICATION ARCHITECTURE

Fig 3.2 can represent the public telephone network. In this architecture, the base transceiver station (BTS) is coupled to a base station controller (BSC), which is then coupled to a telecommunications switch system or gateway that provides connectivity with another transport network (*e.g.* PSTN), or routes calls from one point in the network to another, or to the terminal equipment.

---

[1] The concept of PCM has already been discussed in Chapter 1 section 1.5.

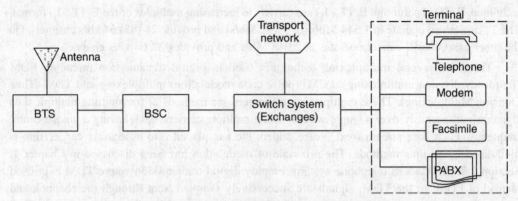

Fig. 3.2. An architecture of a Public Telephone Network

The *base transceiver station* (BTS) is the transmit- and receive- link of a communications system, and may consist a number of transceivers: typically between 1 and 16. A transceiver is a radio device that performs the dual function of a transmitter and a receiver. This means that transceiver has both a transmitter and a receiver in a single package. BTS terminates the radio interface. The BTS connects to the *base station controller* (BSC) over a T_1/E_1 line or link. A BTS typically uses one omnidirectional antenna, which radiates uniformly in all directions. Of course, there may be an instance that requires aiming at specific direction, in that situation a directional antenna may be deployed. The type of antenna used depends also on the service area.

The BSC provides all the control functions and physical links between the switching system and the BTS. The switching system, or a gateway, could be a local exchange (also called *central office* or a *mobile switching centre*) that routes calls from one point in the telecommunication network to another. This switching system can be used to bridge a mobile telephone network with another public telephone network. In the traditional circuit-switched telephone network, one or more switches within the switching system are used to set up a dedicated though temporary connection or circuit for an exchange between two or more parties linked to the network.

It should be noted that the BSC function may be physically located with the BTS. In such an instance, the combined system becomes 'base station system', or simply a 'base station'. The interface between BSC and the switching system is through the '*common channel signalling system number* 7' (SS_7 or C_7) gateway.

SS_7 is a global standard or protocol for telecommunications defined by the Telecommunication Standardization Sector (ITU-T) of the International Telecommunication Union. More is said about SS_7 in chapter 5, section 5.1.2. Other functions of ITU-T have been discussed in Chapter 1, Section 1.6. SS_7 identifies functions to be performed by a signalling-system network and a protocol that enables their performance, especially in support of call-establishment, billing, routing, and information-exchange functions of the public telephone.

3.3.1 Links

The link between exchanges is a *trunk* line. Early trunks were made out of bunches of twisted *unshielded twisted pair* (UTP) cables (see Fig. 3.3), then of coaxial (see Fig. 3.4) or microwaves used with FDM, and now of fibre optics (Fig. 3.5), microwaves (Fig. 3.6), or satellite (Fig. 3.7) with specific multiplexing techniques (*e.g.*, PCM and TDM). Terminal equipments (*e.g.*, PABX, telephone, facsimile, or modem) are connected to the exchange via the *subscriber line* or *local line* like a UTP cable. Whilst telephones have stayed simple, exchanges have become very complex, also very little change in local loop. UTP cable is now frequently installed with two pairs to the home, with the extra pair making it possible to add another line—perhaps for modem use.

Fig. 3.3. An unshielded twisted pair (UTP) cable

Coaxial cable (Fig. 3.4) contains one physical channel (the copper core) that carries the signal surrounded (after a layer of insulation) by another concentric physical channel (a metallic foil or braid), and an outer cover or sheath, all running along the same axis. The outer channel serves as a shield (or ground). Many of these cables or pairs of coaxial tubes can be placed in a single conduit and, with repeaters, can carry information to a great distance. In fact, telephone companies, prior to the introduction of optic fibre, used this type of cable for high bandwidth and video services.

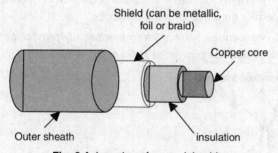

Fig. 3.4. Layering of a coaxial cable

Figure 3.5 represents an optic fibre strand that contains several layers. The core—the actual glass or fibre conductor—is covered with a refractive coating – called cladding. Cladding causes the light to travel in a controlled path along the entire length of the glass core. The next layer is a protective covering that keeps the core and coating from sustaining damage, and also prevents light from escaping the assembly. This covering has a colour coding for identification purposes. The core, coating, and covering are collectively referred to as a "strand". Fibre strand sizes are always referred to in terms of the diameter of the core.

Fibers are assembled into either stranded or ribbon cables. Stranded cables are individual fibers that are bundled together. When up to 12 fibres are grouped together and coated with plastic, a multi-fibre ribbon is constructed. Bundles of stranded and ribbon fibres can be packaged together into either loose or tight buffering cable.

An optic fibre transmits information as light impulses along a strand of glass. Each strand carries much more information than conventional copper wire and is far less subject to electromagnetic interference. Almost all telephone long-distance lines between major population centres are now by optic fibres. Transmission over optic fibre strands requires repeating (or regeneration) at varying intervals. The spacing between these intervals is greater (potentially more than 100 km) than copper based systems. By comparison, a high-speed electrical signal, such as a T_1 signal carried over twisted-pair, must be repeated every 1.8 km. An optic-fibre cable loss is calculated in decibel per kilometre (dB/km), and copper cables are rated in dB per metre (dB/m).

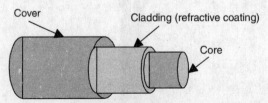

Fig. 3.5. Optic fibre cable

Microwave (radio) systems, as in Fig. 3.6, require a line-of-sight between antennas installed at the two exchanges at the ends of about 40 km route. If line-of-sight is not possible, probably due to diffraction or where providing a point-to-point telecommunication link is beyond the line of sight, one or more radio repeaters must be installed at immediate exchanges or other locations. A radio repeater is a base station radio with a large antenna. Typical types of antenna used in radio relay link installations are parabolic reflectors, shell antennas and horn radiators, which have a diameter of up to 4 metres. Readers requiring in-depth analysis of antennas should consult Kolawole (2002, 2003). Highly directive antennas permit an economical use of the available frequency spectrum, despite long transmission distances.

Microwave link connections form a large number of 'provincial or regional backbones' between the base stations and the provincial radio-relay station and control room.

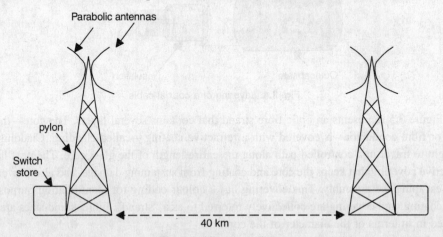

Fig. 3.6. Microwave links

Satellite link is the radio connection between a satellite and an earth station permitting two-way communication between them for telephone channels. Figure 3.7 is an example of a satellite link. Satellite earth station is a communications facility with a microwave radio transmitting and receiving antenna and required receiving and transmitting equipment for communicating with satellites.

A complete satellite communication system consists of two or more earth stations and at least one satellite that provide long distance transmission of voice, data, and television: the system usually serves as a trunk connection between telephone exchanges; if the earth stations are in the same country, it is called a domestic system.

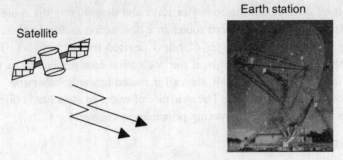

Fig. 3.7. A satellite link

Figure 3.8 follows closely ITU-T [D.155] and demonstrates an intercontinental telephone links between one national network (say, Country #1) and another national network (say, Country #2). The switching arrangement of a national network varies from one country to another. Nevertheless, it has a hierarchical structure comprising part of, if not all designations such as the main, tertiary, secondary, minor and terminal nodes performing different functions. Nodes are interchangeably used as exchanges or switching centres. In this hierarchical structure, switches are interconnecting by 'trunk' links to the terminal (local) node. More is said about this hierarchical structure in the next section.

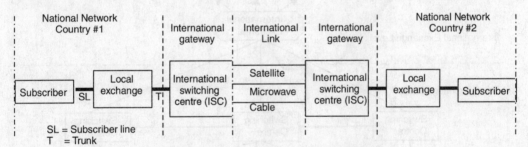

Fig. 3.8. Links between national networks

International gateway is a switching system or an exchange that forms an interface with a national telephone network and/or with one or more other international networks or gateways enabling networks or systems operability and cross-border connectivity. Typically, an international gateway is a high capacity exchange capable of:

- Supporting signalling protocols or their international variants, including SS_7, as well as relevant national signalling protocols.
- Containing devices including
  o Echo suppressor or canceller—a device that reduces the acoustic echo level with negligible effects on the local and distant users' speech, which is generally implemented by adaptive identification of the acoustic echo path response-, and other international variant of voice compression equipment (*e.g.*, Digital Circuit Multiplication Equipment, DCME—often installed at either end of a long-distance link, typically satellite, or submarine cable).

o Transcoder in compliance with A-/μ-law—involving data compression and decompression without exceeding the allowable link losses.

- Supporting numbering plans of each of the countries that can be dialed as well as interpreting the address information transiting the network.
- Supporting different traffic routes or links and determining the route to or toward the destination. Determining which routes to a destination and from source depends on the routing plan or protocol (a set of rules) devised for the network. The basic routing principle is hierarchical. That is, if the destination does not belong to the subscribers of the switch or switches under it, the call is routed upwards; otherwise, it is routed to the node toward that destination. The structure of nodes or switches is discussed in the next section. More is said about routing principles in chapter 4.

3.4 STRUCTURE OF NODES

It may be appropriate, and often is the case, that a public telephone network is divided into three categories, as shown in Fig. 3.9, namely: local exchange network, trunk exchange (also called inter-exchange or regional trunk) network and international network, each level of the hierarchy performing different functions. The network hierarchy may be influenced by market deregulation, or government policy that allows competition among operators or simply by the divestiture. Each exchange-level may have multilayer switching centres or nodes. Nodes are interchangeably used as exchanges or switching centres. This hierarchical classification is necessary even in the digital transmission era because it ensures that [Bennett, 1978]:

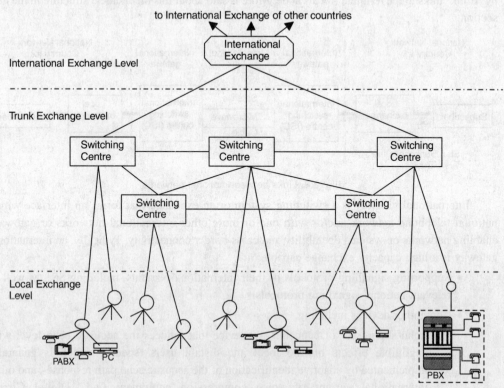

Fig. 3.9. Telecommunications network hierarchical structure

o multi-link connections can be made in systematic manner;

o the number of links which may be connected in tandem imposed by switching and transmission considerations never exceed the allowable, specified number;

o the permissible transmission losses that can be assigned to individual routes must ensure inter-exchange network satisfactory performance is maintained in face of multi-link connections; and

o it is economical to operate, and an improved network control and security can be strategised.

For the international network, though, the arrangement of the international switching centres (ISCs) is left to each country's telecommunications operators/administrations to determine the most suitable utilization of their individual ISCs.

Within the confine of each country, the national network may have hierarchical switching centres (or exchanges) performing different functions. An arrangement can be as shown in Fig. 3.10. There may be subtle differences in network classification from one country to another, or in relation to the recommendation of the ITU-T. For example, Australia telecommunications network classification and that of the ITU-T. The differences are semantics given the Australian geographical expanse. As a consequence, to be consistent with the ITU-T standard definitions, below definitions of the notations in Fig. 3.10 contain alternative names in parentheses signifying that of the ITU-T.

A *main switching centre* (quaternary) switches calls on the final routes for primary switching centres, and if required, secondary switching centres, minor switching centres and terminal exchanges. A main switching centre can serve a certain geographical area, for example a town. Where there are many States or Provinces having concentrated population in their capital cities, main switching centres are often located at the capital cities. The area or areas served by a main switching centre may not coincide with town, city or provincial boundaries, but may depend on the basic objectives governing the design of numbering and switching sections of the network plan. Network numbering plan has been discussed in Chapter 2 Section 2.5. If the switching system is controlled, numbering and routing functions may be separate; so, exact correlation may not be necessary.

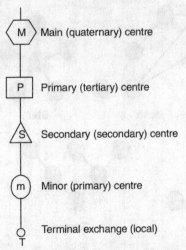

Fig. 3.10. Hierarchy of switching nodes

A *primary switching centre* (tertiary) switches calls on the final routes for secondary switching centres and also, if required, minor switching centres and terminal exchanges.

A *secondary switching centre* (secondary) switches calls on the final routes for minor switching centres and also, if required, terminal exchanges.

A *minor switching centre* (primary) switches calls on the final routes for terminal exchanges.

A *terminal exchange* (local) is an exchange that performs no through-connection of calls on inter-exchange circuits. It terminates both lines and trunks and provides the subscriber access to the public telephone network.

There had been gradual shift in switching centre architecture since early 1980s where the analogue exchanges have been replaced with digital switching centres interconnected with digital transmission links. Digitisation enables an increased variety of facilities and services to be made available to the telecommunications user, resulting in ISDN (Integrated Services Digital Network).

3.4.1 Location of Exchanges

There is a relationship between subscriber density and the economic radius of the exchange area. This relationship helps to determine the approximate boundary of an exchange, which can be adjusted, if need be, for practical consideration. This consideration comes to play when reviewing sections of a network to determine the need for new exchanges, or boundary adjustment. The major objective in determining the location of a terminal exchange is to minimise subscribers-line, and trunk and junction costs.

3.4.2 Network Topology

The way the elements (*e.g.*, physical or signal) comprising a network is arranged or mapped determines its topology. Topology is a set up in which a given node has one or more links to others, and can appear in a variety of different shapes. Topologies consist of generators (a computer, for example), vertical edges (possibly a wire connecting to the rest of the network), and horizontal edges that serve to carry information and reinforce the structure of the topology. There are certain basic topologies—namely bus, star, ring, mesh or tree—as seen in Fig. 3.11, which can be combined to form more hybrid or complex topologies.

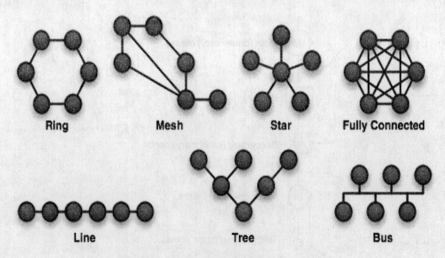

Fig. 3.11. Network nodes of different shapes

In the context of the public telephone network, topology is determined only by the graphical mapping of the configuration of physical and/or logical connections between nodes. Two networks may be different in terms of the distances between nodes, physical interconnections, transmission rates, and/or signalling, yet their topologies may be similar.

Consider two network topologies—mesh and star—formed by connecting six exchanges as shown in Fig 3.12. In the *mesh network* [as in Fig 3.12(*a*)] each exchange has a direct connection to every other exchange, whilst in the *star network* [as in Fig 3.12(*b*)] all exchanges are connected via a central switching device. In terms of switching complexity and cost, relatively complex switching capacity is needed at each of the six exchanges for the mesh arrangement whilst a large and costly central switch is needed for the star arrangement given that its network switching is concentrated at the central node.

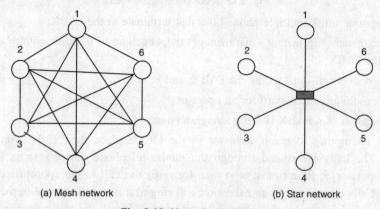

(a) Mesh network   (b) Star network

Fig. 3.12. Network topologies

Regardless of the network design type, the goal is to control *grade of service*, GoS. More is said about GoS in Section 3.6. Specifically, the ability to provide an overall grade of service for all traffic offered to the network, or grade of service offered to certain streams of traffic. This can be achieved by the choice of a routing scheme that

    o reduces the effect of adverse network conditions,

    o allows flexibility, and provides greater resilience and service protection, especially in the case of forecast errors or focused overload.

More is discussed about traffic routing in Chapter 4.

3.4.3 Private Automatic Branch Exchange

As noted, the links between the switching centres are trunks, and the links between the minor switching centres (primary) and terminal exchanges are local lines. Each trunk is allocated to, or seized by, a call only for the duration of that call and, at the end of the call; it is dropped and becomes available for another user. There is always diversity-meaning that at any point in time not everyone is using the system—so the total number of lines available is a fraction of the number of connections in existence. The same diversity principle applies to any government agencies or business organizations, it is unnecessary to provide a dedicated 'line' to the PSTN for every appliance installed in those agencies or organizations. Instead, a sort of 'local exchange' switch is used—quaintly referred to as the *public branch exchange* (PBX) or the *private automatic branch exchange* (PABX). In an office environment, the PABX system connects multiple incoming phone lines to multiple telephone extensions (see Fig. 3.13). A PABX includes:

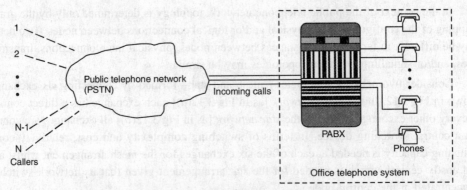

Fig. 3.13. A company based PABX

- Telephone trunk-multiple phone-lines that terminate at the PABX;
- A computer with memory that manages the switching of the calls within, and in and out of the PABX;
- The network of lines within the PABX; and
- A console or switchboard for an operator.

The operation of a PABX is fairly straightforward.

Callers attempting to reach someone in the Office place their calls from any type of telephones. The calls are routed through the public telephone network (*e.g.*, PSTN) to the company's operator or receptionist who then forwards the call to the appropriate extension or department. Calls transferred to an extension will ring at a particular phone in the office. If the extension owner picks up the phone the call is connected. If not, the call is usually transferred to a voice machine or voice mail.

In essence, PBX switches do little more than cross-connect the incoming lines. The basic operations of other terminal equipments; namely telephone, facsimile, and modem, have been discussed in Chapter 1.

PABX equipments under discussion are analogues primarily for voice communication; they are bandwidth limited. Inter-company communications include voice and data transmission and reception, and with the advent of data switching through local area networking (LAN) and/or wide area networking (WAN), video application has been a necessity. Therefore, the need to have PABXs that will integrate data, voice and video services results in the employment of digital switching techniques, capable of handling these services without substantial outlay. Current PABXs have analogue to digital conversion (ADC) module included. Such PABXs are known as *private digital exchanges* (PDXs). The principle of an ADC has been discussed in chapter 1, section 1.5.2.

3.5 NETWORK STANDARDS

Today's global communications world has obscured traditional boundaries in network access between Telecommunication Network Operators, Private Network Providers, Satellite and Cable TV Networks and Information Technologies. Nevertheless, to facilitate the interoperability of network technologies certain standards must be met. In this text, the network standards that relate to the public switched telephone network (PSTN) are explored, given that major elements of public telephone network form the backbone of the emerging networks. These standards have to be designed to allow tailoring by other management standards organizations to meet their regional, national, or specific-technology needs. The overall objective of meeting any standards is ensuring the maintenance of standard of service. The standards chosen should comply with international standards set by the ITU-T so that international telephone communication is not impeded or compromised.

To ensure the network provides the quality of service required by the subscribers, amongst the plethora of standards, two—namely transmission performance standard and grade of service (GoS) standard—are explored. All standards are subject to revision. The readers are encouraged to investigate the possibility of applying the most recent editions of the standards considered below.

3.5.1 Transmission Performance Standards

A telephone network originates from a number of telephone services that need to communicate with each other. The overall transmission performance standard specifies the loss from the speaker to the listener. Establishing transmission standards is a complex problem since the objective is to specify the quality of communication from the speaker to the listener, which involves an essentially subjective judgment. It is affected by several factors other than the network and the telephone itself. For example, background room noise, the standard of hearing and speech, the method of using telephone instrument have a significant effect on the quality of a conversation. Despite the difficulty, transmission standards are necessary and could be expressed as a limit condition that would require that no call in the network experiences transmission worse than that produced by (a) one from the local exchange, and (b) one from (e.g., the attenuator) from the inter exchange network, see Fig. 3.14. The standard does not specify how many calls should experience the limit, merely that no call must exceed it.

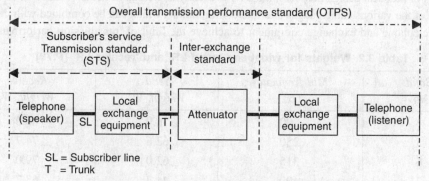

Fig. 3.14. Transmission Performance Standard

3.5.2 Subscriber's Service Transmission Performance Standard

The subscriber's service transmission standard (STS) is expressed by means of Reference Equivalents, which are 15.0 dB sending and 2.6 dB receiving. Reference Equivalents are produced by comparing the sending and receiving performance of the STS against that of a standard apparatus at the ITU-T laboratory in Geneva. Theoretical methods [including Richards, 1978] have been proposed that enable reference equivalents to be calculated instead of having to be determined by subjective measurements.

The acceptable loudness ratings of telephone-sets at send and receive must comply with ITU-T recommendation for transmission planning and regulatory purposes. Loudness ratings, LR, for telephone sets are used for two reasons [P.79]: first, to provide the transmission planner with an adequate measure of how the sets perform in the network; and second, to enable valid and unambiguous comparison between sets. A general algorithm for calculating LR is given by [P.79] as:

$$LR = -\frac{10}{m} \log_{10} \left[\sum_{i=N_1}^{N_2} 10^{0.1m(S_i - W_i)} \right] \tag{3.1}$$

where m is a constant—in the order of 0.2.

The summation is to be performed at frequencies F_i, spaced 1/3 octave apart.

W_i = weighting coefficient: this is different for the various send LR and receive LR. The weighting coefficients are given in Table 3.2, when $m = 0.175$. New Recommendation gives the W_i weights for calculating sending and receiving loudness ratings extending to 8000 Hz terminals.

$S_i = -L_i$ = the sensitivity at frequency F_i of the electro-acoustic path under consideration, where L_i is the loss at frequency F_i of the electro-acoustic path under consideration. The sending sensitivity of a hand-free telephone (HFT) set is about 5 dB higher than that of the corresponding handset telephone—the actual value will depend on the type of handset used. The average acoustic speech level from a terminal user is about 3 dB higher when using a HFT than when using a handset telephone.

The receiving sensitivity of a HFT without automatic gain control is within a range of 15 to 30 dB. For hands-free terminals equipped with an automatic gain control for the receive level (the gain being controlled by the incoming speech voltage), loudness ratings may not be applicable.

To meet the STS limit condition, considering the line losses and coupling leakage as small or negligible, the limit on the local exchange can easily be estimated knowing the loudness value at each end. For practical design purposes, the STS is usually expressed in terms of the maximum loop resistance of the various cable gauges and line configurations which can be combined with different types of telephone and exchange equipment to achieve the limit of transmission performance.

Table 3.2. Weights for wideband 'send LR' and 'receive LR' [P.79]

Band No.	Mid-frequency (Hz)	Send Weight, W_i	Receive Weight, W_i
4	200	76.9	85.0
5	250	62.6	74.7
6	315	62.0	79.0
7	400	44.7	63.7
8	500	53.1	73.7
9	630	48.5	69.1
10	800	47.6	68.0
11	1000	50.1	68.7
12	1250	59.1	75.1
13	1600	56.7	70.4
14	2000	72.2	81.4
15	2500	72.6	76.5
16	3150	89.2	93.3
17	4000	117.0	113.8

3.5.3 Inter Exchange Network Performance Standard

The limit of 15 dB represents the maximum loss between terminal exchanges (represented by the 15 dB attenuator in Fig. 3.14). This 15 dB overall loss is the summation of each insertion loss of each component in the network between two terminal exchanges. As an illustration, the inter exchange network standards can be distributed as in Fig. 3.15. The loss weight distribution in this figure closely resembles the Australian network outlined in Bennett (1978).

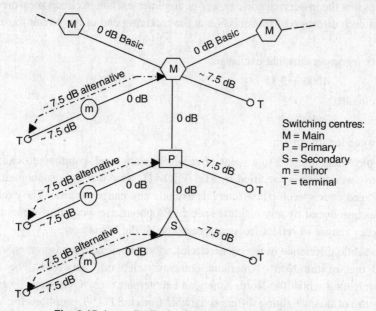

Fig. 3.15. Loss distribution between terminal exchanges

The frequency at which each component is measured depends on the medium of propagation used as each has its own characteristic change of attenuation over the audio frequency, f, range; for example,

$$\begin{cases} \text{loaded - cable} \\ \text{open - wire} \\ \text{carrier} \end{cases} \qquad \begin{cases} f = 1.6\,\text{kHz} \\ f = 1.0\,\text{kHz} \\ f = 0.8\,\text{kHz} \end{cases}$$

As noted in Fig. 3.15, the nominal operating loss of 0 dB basic indicates that circuits are not fitted with echo suppressors or cancellers. However, where links require echo suppressors, the nominal operating basic loss is 0.5 dB. Echo suppressors are required on international calls but not on domestic (national) calls. This nominal loss varies with length of transmission, as shown in Table 3.3.

Table 3.3. Nominal operating loss

Length of circuit (km)	Nominal operating loss (dB)
< 560	0
560 – 1200	0.5
> 1200	1.0

Also as in Fig 3.15, for the alternative distribution between two terminals, we can take the maximum permissible total line loss of ~ 7.5 dB, where that of terminal links can be 6 dB, and the remainder of 1.5 dB is fixed allowance for exchange loss.

3.5.4 In-service Noise Standard

Telephone circuit noise is psophometrically weighted by the ear. The performance standard for noise requires that the in-service noise power of any inter-exchange circuit measured as a mean over any hour in each direction of transmission at the receiving end of the circuit must not exceed the following.

For circuits serving a terminal exchange:

$$4000 + 3.11 \ L \qquad\qquad\qquad\qquad \text{pWOp} \qquad\qquad (3.2)$$

All other circuits:

$$2000 + 3.0 \ L \qquad\qquad\qquad\qquad \text{pWOp} \qquad\qquad (3.3)$$

where L is the route length (in km)

pWOp is picowatts referred to a point of zero reference level, psophometrically weighted. The psophometric weighting is specified by ITU-T [O.41]. Note that the psophometric weighted noise level averaged over speech pause intervals exclude any hangover time. The exclusion helps to eliminate bias introduced by any residual speech. Psophometric weighting varies the effect of different frequency ranges to reflect frequency response of the human ear.

There is a subtle difference in telephone circuit noise impairment measurements as specified by ITU-T and that of the North American domestic telephone networks. The ITU-T uses psophometric weighting whilst the North American counterpart uses "C-message" weighting. The frequency response of this weighting differs somewhat from the ITU-T psophometric weighting in Recommendation O.41 [O.41]. Recognizing that the relationship of the output readings of the differently weighted instruments will change for other noise spectra, a conversion formula is proposed [O.41]:

$$P_{\text{ITU-T}} \ (\text{dBm}) \ = \ C_{\text{message}} \ (\text{dBrn}) - 90 \qquad\qquad (3.4)$$

where $P_{\text{ITU-T}}$ = Psophometer reading (in dBm).

   C_{message} = C-message noise meter reading (in dBrn). Note that dBrn is decibels referred to -90 dBm or decibels above a reference power of 10-12 watts.

Note that the C-message weighting is not the same as the '3 kHz Flat' weighting, which is frequently used in the North American domestic telephone networks for the investigation of the presence of low-frequency noise (power induction, etc.) on the circuit under test. It is characterized as a 3 kHz low-pass weighting of Butterworth shape[2] attenuating above 3 kHz at 12 dB per octave. The specification for this weighting is given in [O.41] and for measurement device is given in [P.561].

The current public telephone network is mixed analogue/digital PSTN, which interworks with ISDN—an international communications standard for sending voice, video and data over existing telephone wires or digital telephone lines. Technological advances are improving the outlook of telecommunications in areas beyond the boundaries currently known including switching and

---

[2] Butterworth shape has a monotonically changing magnitude function: maximally flat amplitude, with a slower roll-off.

components fabrication and interconnectivity. Nanoscience raises the future prospect. Nanoscience and nanotechnology involve studying and working with matter on an ultra-small scale—a scale in the order of ~ 1-100 nm. A nanometer (nm) is 10^{-9} m (one billionth of a metre). More is said about nanotechnology in chapter 10.

The above noise performance limits may not satisfy the current telephone paradigm, given that a wide range of new systems that utilize digital processes and radio transmission are introduced into telephone networks. The actual in-service noise standard would depend on the ITU-T Study Group 12 recommendations.

3.5.5 Grade of Service Standard

Service Standard demonstrates a set of quantifiable commitments that outline the minimum requirements expected by the users of the services from the service providers whether in terms of voice quality, data transmission, telephone connection without dropout, etc. In telecommunication engineering, the quality of voice service is specified by two measures: the grade of service (GoS) and the quality of service (QoS).

The measurement of traffic in public telephone networks allows network operators to determine and maintain the QoS and in particular the GoS that the network operators offer their subscribers. The performance of a network depends on whether all origin-destination pairs are receiving a satisfactory service.

3.6 GRADE OF SERVICE

Grade of service (GoS) is a measure of the quality of communications service. GoS uses a number of traffic engineering parameters to provide a measure of adequacy of plant under specified conditions; these GoS parameters may be expressed as probability of blocking, probability of delay, etc [E.720]. Blocking and delay are caused by the fact that the traffic handling capacity of a network/network component is finite and that the demand traffic is stochastic (or probabilistic) by nature.

The users of telecommunication services can experience the effects of GoS parameters depending on their perception of events such as:

(*a*) the failure of a call demand or excessive delay to satisfy a call demand;

(*b*) failure of call attempts or excessive delay to satisfy call attempts;

(*c*) failure of automatic re-attempts or excessive delay to satisfy automatic re-attempts.

These three events are dependent on user conditions and network conditions.

Grade of service (GoS) may be applied to the busy hour, or to some other specified period, or a set of traffic conditions. Given that the demand traffic is stochastic (or probabilistic) by nature, a network's GoS can be expressed in terms of the probability that a connection cannot be made between a calling party and called party due to insufficient provision of network plant. The connection can also fail to be achieved due to the called party already using the service, or the network plant failing to operate properly. GoS can also be calculated in other ways, partly discussed next.

3.6.1 Calculating the Grade of Service

A more detailed analysis of network traffic is given in Chapter 9. Part of the work in Chapter 9 deals with the grade of service analysis: a result that is used in calculating Grade of service (GoS) in this section. GoS can be measured in different ways.

First, if a number of calls is lost due to congestion in a particular busy hour, the GoS can be measured using

$$GoS = \frac{N_l}{N_o} \qquad (3.5)$$

where N_l is the number of lost calls, and N_o is the number of offered calls.

Second, if a specified group of circuits, or routes, on network loses calls when all circuits in a group were busy, then a different approach in calculating GoS is required. This approach precipitates on the assumptions that:

o Since telephone traffic is the aggregate of calls originated by the users of the network, all call arrivals and terminations are independent random events,

o The average number of calls does not change,

o The network is fully available and can be accessible from every inlet,

o Any call that encounters congestion is immediately lost.

Using the mathematics of probability and considering the randomness inherent in the system, the Erlang-B formula, which in itself is based on the probability of congestion in a group of circuits, can be applied to describe the Grade of Service, GoS, experienced by the network. Specifically:

$$GoS = P_b = \frac{A^n / N!}{\sum_{k=0}^{N} A^k / k!} \qquad (3.6)$$

where A = expected traffic intensity or density in Erlang; dependent on the calls average arrival rate and the calls' duration.

N = number of trunks or circuits in the group.

k = number of busy trunks or circuits.

P_b = probability of blockage.

Equation (3.6) allows operators to determine whether each of their circuit groups meets the required Grade of Service, simply by monitoring the reference traffic intensity. How (3.6) is derived becomes clearer in chapter 9.

For the Australian automatic network, the grade of service standard chosen is to achieve an overall probability, P_b, of call failure of between $0.01 < P_b < 0.0125$; that is, call failure of between 1 in 100 (0.01) and 1 in 80 (0.0125). The standard set for delay in receiving data tone requires that not more than 0.01 (i.e., ≤ 0.01) of calls will experience a delay, δ, of more than 1 second (i.e., $\delta \geq 1$ sec.) from the time the terminal exchange receives the service signal until dial tone is applied to the subscriber line. There is no equivalent formal standard of objective set for post-dialling delay. Despite this, a delay in excess of 9 seconds is considered unacceptable to users.

3.6.2 Traffic Characteristics

Telephone traffic is the aggregate of calls originated independently by the users of the public telephone network. This traffic causes randomly distributed occupancies of circuits and plants in various parts of the network. In practice, a feature observed from this random behaviour is that larger streams of traffic can be handled more efficiently than smaller ones. Thus, the provision of additional circuits on a route being offered of a fixed level of traffic provides a diminishing return in terms of traffic carried for each of these circuits. The incremental traffic T_{r_s} carried by a group circuits offered κ Erlang of traffic with the addition g of each group can be approximated as

$$T_{r_s} = \kappa e^{-g} \tag{3.7}$$

Example: Consider a 10 erlang of traffic offered by a group of circuits. Plot the traffic characteristic for each block of circuits added to the group up to the tenth.

Solution: $\kappa = 10$; substitute this value in (3.7) and plot for $1 \le g \le 10$ as in Fig. 3.16.

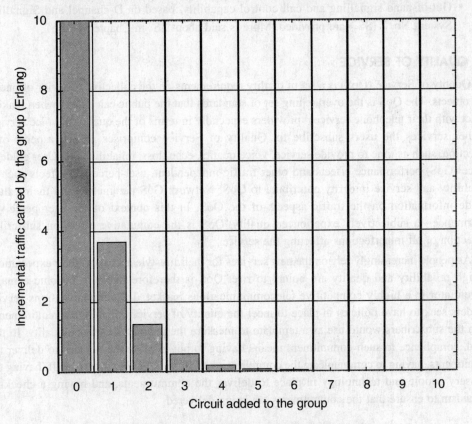

Fig. 3.16. Increment in the traffic with addition of each circuit
for a fully available group of circuits

To design a network for minimum cost, this characteristic makes it desirable to assemble traffic, wherever appropriate, into large parcels so improving efficiency and thus requiring the minimum number of devices to handle it.

ISDN has many traffic characteristics that are different from that of the PSTN, and from other dedicated networks including Circuit Switched Public Data Network (CSPDN), Packet Switched Public Data Network (PSPDN), etc. ISDN provides integrated access to a wide variety of telecommunication services through a small set of standardized user-network interfaces. As a result, when defining GoS parameters for ISDN, certain characteristics must be noted, for example that [E.720]:

- Services have heterogeneous traffic demand profiles and diverse performance requirements.

- The traffic streams generated by user demands for bearer services and teleservices utilize layer 1, 2 and 3 resources.

- The configuration and implementation of a user's terminal and its man-machine interface may vary from one service to another service and one user to another user.

- Out-of-band signalling and call control capability, based on D-channel and Signalling System No. 7 (SS_7) are provided. More is said about SS_7 in Chapter 5.

3.7   QUALITY OF SERVICE

Quality of Service (QoS) is a set of quality requirements on the collective behavior of one or more objects. The QoS is the overarching set of standards that the public can expect when making contact with their telephone services' providers especially in terms of the quality of voice service, or other services the users subscribe to. Quality of Service comprises all the aspects of a connection, such as time to provide service, voice quality, echo, loss, reliability, etc. User grade of service (GoS) performance effects and other traffic-independent, user-perceived effects such as availability and service integrity contribute to QoS. Network GoS parameters and their values provide information on the traffic aspects of the QoS. In this context of the user perceived performance—a subjectively experienced quality, QoS is the cumulative effect on subscriber satisfaction of all imperfections affecting the service.

As people increasingly rely on the new services for their lifestyle and work, their expectations for high reliability and quality are bound to rise. QoS is therefore likely to become a major differentiator in a highly competitive telecommunications market. Telecommunications service providers seek to have policies in place to meet the quality of service commitment requirements, which the subscribers would use as a template to measure the guaranteed service quality. In this regard, compliance to such commitment means having to put in place the policies to deliver the commitments, having to communicate the commitments to all staff, having to train staff, having the necessary people and technology in place to deliver the commitments, and having a checking mechanism to ensure that the commitments are being delivered.

3.8   SUMMARY

This chapter has identified and described the principles that govern the structure and development of public telecommunication networks, particularly the way in which various components interact. The performance of a network depends on whether all origin-destination pairs are receiving a satisfactory service.

For quality control purpose, the measurement of traffic in public telephone networks allows network operators to determine and maintain the *quality of service* (QoS) and in particular the *grade of service* (GoS) they offer the network users. The QoS of a network must be maintained or else operators will lose subscribers. Exchanges in the public telephone networks make use of trunking concepts to help minimise the cost of the equipment to the operator. More is said about trunking concept in chapter 4. Modern switches generally have full availability and do not make use of grading concepts.

QUESTIONS

1. What is Grade of Service and how is it measured?
2. Given that modern switches are fully utilized, suggest how a network performance can be measured?
3. Explain how a public telephone network's nodes are configured. Which type would you suggest for your town assuming a gradual utilization increase in telecommunication services?
4. What does T_1 stand for? What is the difference between T_1 and E_1? What would influence your decision of which carrier format to use?
5. Describe the operating principle of a PABX. Currently, your company is contemplating restructuring and replacing the manned PABX. Explain the changes to recommend. And, design the new system.
6. What are the main components of a public telephone network exchange and what are their functions?

4

ROUTING

Routing involves the selection of a path from the originating node to the destination node in a network, or between networks. In other word, it is the selection of a particular circuit group, for a given call attempt or traffic stream, at an exchange in the network; and also, in finding a convenient path from a source to destination host. The choice of a circuit group may be affected by information on the availability of downstream elements of the network. Finding the convenient routing path that is responsive to varying traffic conditions has led to a host of routing schemes and strategies.

To have a feel for what traffic routing is, let us consider the two network arrangements shown in Fig. 4.1; mesh and star, connecting six exchanges. In the mesh network, as in Fig. 4.1(*a*), each exchange has a direct connection to every other exchange. It could be said that traffic from each exchange is connected over the shortest possible available route, which requires a minimal number of switching stages. The disadvantage of a mesh arrangement is that total traffic originating from an exchange is split into several small groups, which require a greater number of circuits than that required by a single large group. For the star network arrangement in Fig. 4.1(*b*), all exchanges are connected via a central switching device. The traffic in the star-network is maintained as a single large group, which requires the minimal number of circuits that traverse longer distances, making the arrangement more costly.

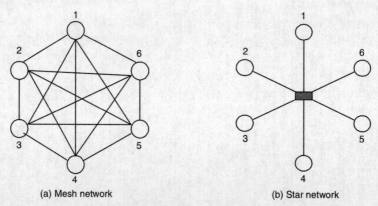

(a) Mesh network   (b) Star network

Fig. 4.1. Network topologies

The two examples given by Fig. 4.1 have demonstrated that both types of networks have advantages and disadvantages, and a compromise between the two extremes that will produce a network that is cheaper than either is the objective of alternatively routed networks.

This chapter therefore explores the different routing schemes and how they respond to traffic conditions internally detected by the exchange, or to status signals from other exchanges.

4.1   ROUTING STRUCTURE

Many connections in circuit switched network need paths through more than one switch. The possibility of flexible control of network traffic has given rise to the formulation of many theoretical and applied routing schemes. As noted in chapter 3, exchanges in telephone networks are hierarchically structured, but routing structure can be hierarchical or nonhierarchical. A routing structure is hierarchical if, for all traffic streams, all calls offered to a given route, at a specific node, overflow to the same set of routes irrespective of the routes already tested. Figure 4.2 is an illustration of a hierarchical structure, and closely follows one given in [E.170]. The routes in the set will always be tested in the same sequence, for example in Fig. 4.2, 1 to 2 at every node level. The last choice route is final in the sense that no traffic streams using this route may overflow further. Overflow occurs when the direct first-choice route is busy.

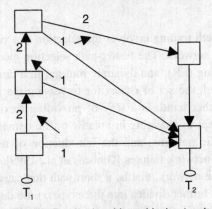

Fig. 4.2. Routing in a hierarchical network

In Fig. 4.3, as an illustration, consider calls initiated from exchange A and going to exchange B. These calls have a direct first-choice route from A to B (AB). An alternative route is from A through C to B (ACB). Here for simplicity, exchange C is considered a tandem exchange at a higher hierarchical level than A, B and D, where tandem C is destined for other parts of the network. Direct routes at the lower level (*e.g.*, AB) overflow via the hierarchical route (ACB). In networks of this type of arrangement, it is advisable for exchange A to apply service protection on the circuit group AC to restrict traffic overflowing to final choice routes. This control of grade of service, GoS, allows optimal (minimum cost) dimensioning for planned traffic loads in addition to giving protection against heavy overloads.

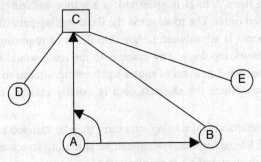

Fig. 4.3. Routing overflow principle

When the mutual overflow between circuit groups originates at the same exchange then the associated routing structure is non-hierarchical.

It must be noted that the concept of hierarchical routing may not be directly related to the concept of a hierarchy of switching centres or exchanges. For large size networks, routing can be simplified by reducing the size of the networks and by breaking into a hierarchy of networks, where each level is responsible for its own routing. Hierarchical structures are well suited for visualizing the organization and decomposition of complex networks or systems.

At the telephone exchange reside pre-computed *routing tables*—tables of pre-defined routes for a connection—(also called *distance tables*), which the exchange uses. Routing tables are generated by batch processing at a switching centre, which are based on the topology of the network, the numbering plan, and traffic profile.

4.2 ROUTING SCHEME

Connection or bearer-path routing involves the selection of a path from the originating node to the destination node in a network. The bearer-path selection methods can be categorized into two broad types: fixed routing (FR), and dynamic routing. In a circuit-switched network where fixed routing scheme is used, the set of routes for traversing the network is always the same. Dynamic routing, on the other hand, is a way of providing flexibility at the switched level. Flexibility is required to adapt to changing in volatile traffic demands; to cope with forecasting uncertainties, shifts in traffic patterns, and the introduction of new services; and to provide resilience against individual network failures [Gibbens et al., 1999]. Dynamic routing is meant to find the best path through the network, that is, a short path that causes the least damage to future calls. The dynamic routing is further divided into three types: time-dependent routing (TDR), state-dependent routing (SDR), and event-dependent routing (EDR). These bearer-path selection methods are associated with routing tables, which consist of a route and rules to select one path from the route for a given connection or bandwidth-allocation request.

This section also gained from the publication of ITU-T Recommendations especially [E.170], [E.412], [E.525] that emphasized the importance of routing. The next few subsections explain the different types of bearer-path selection (routing) schemes.

4.2.1 Fixed Routing

In the fixed routing scheme, the shortest path is usually chosen, and a single permanent route is configured for each source to destination pair. Consider a group of calls from node A to node B as in Fig 4.3. The path from A to B is specified in advance ensuring that the calls are passed through in the pre-planned order. The route set in the fixed routing pattern will always be the same. Changes to path only occur if a hardware failure disables it or requiring manual intervention, or there is a change in network topology. Any changes to the route would become permanent to the routing scheme, implying that a new set of routes has been introduced to the fixed routing scheme superseding the previous. Since the shortest path is usually chosen, communication costs are minimized.

Hierarchical or nonhierarchical routing structures may be realised based on the fixed-routing type of schemes. In both hierarchical and nonhierarchical routing structures, the route set and route selection sequence are determined on a preplanned basis and maintained over a long period of time. Fixed routing cannot adapt to load changes.

As traffic routing is closely related to network design in fixed networks, it becomes clear that using a fixed routing pattern, determined by busy-hour and busy-season traffic measurements, cannot allow the efficient accommodation in unexpected traffic situations. Besides, advances in the technology of modern telecommunication systems have led to considerable interest in schemes that can dynamically control the routing of calls within a network and/or between networks. Dynamism in routing schemes means the ability

o to adjust routing patterns within the network in accordance with varying and uncertain offered traffics,

o to make better use of spare capacity in the network resulting from dimensioning upgrades or forecasting errors, and

o to provide extra flexibility and robustness to respond to failures or overloads.

Ultimately one of the goals for any dynamic routing scheme is to balance traffic load on different alternative routes—which are specified in the routing tables—and the end result is that these alternative routes will have equivalent *quality of service* (QoS) under steady state. For example we can use blocking probability as a criterion to adjust the traffic distribution. The switching equipment at the exchange in case of link failure or congestion can dynamically select these alternative routes, or when changing traffic patterns and demands make pre-computed routing inefficient.

4.2.2 Dynamic Routing

Dynamic routing is a process for selecting the most appropriate path or route for a group of calls or packet to travel around a network. This process was well described by Ash and Chemouil (2004) in their paper, and is used in this section. When a telephone call arrives at its originating exchange (OE)—as A in Fig. 4.4, the originating switch implementing the routing method executes

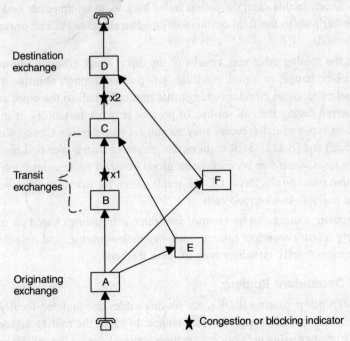

Destination exchange

Transit exchanges

Originating exchange

★ Congestion or blocking indicator

Fig. 4.4. Dynamic routing and automatic rerouting technique

the route selection rules (or protocols) associated with the routing table for the call to determine a route.

In a routing method, the set of routes that can be assigned to the call may be altered according to a certain route set alteration rule. Depending on whether a switch functions as an OE, e.g., A, a transit-exchange or switch (TE), e.g., B and/or C, or a destination exchange or switch (DE), e.g., G—as in Fig. 4.4, different routing tables are used for calls.

The OE normally determines the dynamic routing method used for a call and selects the appropriate routing table. A network is operated with progressive call control, originating call control, or a mix of the two control methods. A direct route from the source is through exchanges ABCG to the destination as in Fig 4.4. Alternative routing takes place when all appropriate circuits in a group are busy. Several circuit groups may be tested sequentially. The testing order will be fixed or time-dependent. For instance, if a signal indicating congestion is received from Exchange B, meaning that route B to C is congested (x_1-indicator), a call from A to G is rerouted via H to C. If further in the process a signal indicating congestion is received from Exchange C, meaning that route C to G is congested (x_2-indicator), the call can be rerouted at A through F to destination exchange G.

In a network with progressive call control, a switch selects a trunk group to an appropriate next switch. In a network with originating call control, the originating switch maintains control of the call. When an *automatic rerouting* (ARR) (or *crankback*) is used, for example, at a transit-switch (H or F), the preceding switch maintains control of the call even if the calls are blocked at all the routes outgoing from the transit-exchange, TE.

ARR is a routing facility enabling connection of call attempts encountering congestion during the initial call setup phase. Crankback is a backtracking procedure used when a connection setup request is blocked because a node along a selected path cannot accept the request due to insufficient resources. In this case, the path is rolled back to an intermediate node, which attempts to discover another path to the final destination. In general, networks can operate with a mix of both control methods.

Routes in the routing table may consist of the direct trunk group, a two-trunk-group route through a transit-exchange, or a multiple-trunk-group route through multiple transit-exchanges. Care must be taken to avoid circular routings that return the call to the point at which blocking previously occurred during the call set-up. To prevent network instability or to set up priorities between different types of calls, routes may be subject to Selective Circuit Reservation (SCR) restrictions [E.525] and [E.412]. SCR requires that one more than a specified number of circuits— the 'reservation level'—are free on each trunk group before a route connection is allowed. This prevents calls that route on the direct OE-DE trunk group, for example, from being swamped by alternate routed multiple-trunk-group calls.

Dynamic traffic routing can be grouped into three subheadings based on their routing table category, namely: *event-dependent routing*, *state-dependent routing*, and *time-dependent routing*. The next subsections briefly introduce each of these methods.

4.2.3 Event-Dependent Routing

In *event-dependent routing* (EDR), the routing tables are updated locally on the basis of whether calls succeed or fail on a given route choice. In EDR, the routing tables are designed by the originating exchange using network information obtained during the call setup function. In this type of routing, for example, a call is offered first to a fixed, pre-planned route often encompassing only a direct route, if it exists. As an illustration, consider a call originating from C and terminating at E in a fully connected mesh-network of Fig. 4.5, and having pre-planned routes as in Table 4.1.

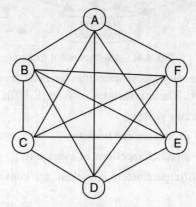

Fig. 4.5. Event-dependent routing for a fully connected mesh network

There are two pre-planned choices for C to E route: a direct route from C to E, and alternative route C through D to E. If no circuit is available on the pre-planned direct route, the overflow traffic is offered to a currently selected alternate CDE route. If the call is blocked on the current alternate CDE route choice, another alternate route CFE is selected from a set of available alternate routes (CFE, CBE, CAE) according to the given routing table rules of Table 4.1. The current alternate route choice can be updated randomly, cyclically, or by some other means, and may be maintained as long as a call is established successfully on the route.

Table 4.1. C to E route pattern

Choice	Current	After call failure
1.	CE	CE
2.	CDE	CFE, CBE, CAE

Many national telecommunications carriers have utilized event-dependent routing; some are still in operation. Examples of those in operation include *LastabehŠngige Automatische Wegesuche* (*LAW*, in English, *Automatic Last Choice Routing*) by Deutsche Telecom National Network; *Acheminement Multiple Intelligent* (AIM, in English, *Multiple Intelligent Routing – MIR*) by France Telecom Long Distance Network; and *Dynamic Alternative Routing* (*DAR*) by British Telecom UK National Network.

4.2.4 State-Dependent Routing

The *state-dependent routing* (SDR) scheme calculates alternate routing paths for each switch pair independently, based upon an average trunk group usage during a previous time interval. The alternate routing paths are ordered, and are attempted sequentially by each call between the switch pair. SDR routing tables are altered automatically according to the state of the network. Figure 4.6 can be used to explain the function of an SDR. In the figure, a centralized routing processor is employed to select optimum routing patterns on the basis of the actual occupancy levels of the circuit groups (and exchanges) in the network, which are monitored on a periodical basis (*e.g.*, 10, 20 seconds). Information on the network status may be collected at the central processor or distributed to exchanges in the network.

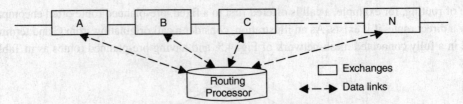

Fig. 4.6. State-dependent routing

The SDR technique inherently incorporates fundamental principles of network management in determining routing patterns. These principles include [E.170]:

o avoiding occupied circuit groups;

o not using overloaded exchanges for transit;

o restriction of routing direct connections in overloads.

Typically, qualitative traffic parameters are taken into consideration when determining the optimal routing pattern.

There have been various implementations of SDR distinguished by whether the computation of routing tables is distributed among the network exchanges, or centralised, and whether the computation is done in a centralised routing processor and periodically or call by call. The difference in implementation methods leads to variants of SDR scheme such as centralised periodic, distributed periodic and distributed call-by-call.

In general, SDR methods calculate a route cost for each call based on various factors such as the load-state or congestion state of trunk groups in the network.

Several telecommunications carriers have utilised SDR schemes. Examples of those in operation include Stentor Canada National Network, Bell Canada Network, and various providers in USA including Qwest Communications National Network, MCI US National Network, and Sprint National Network.

4.2.5 Time-Dependent Routing

In *time-dependent routing* (TDR) scheme, routing patterns are altered at fixed times during the day (or week) to allow changing traffic demands to be provided for. Normally, these changes are pre-planned and implemented consistently over a long time period. To explain this dynamic scheme, consider for example, each originating and terminating exchange pair, *i.e.*, B to F in Fig. 4.7. A particular route pattern is pre-planned depend...ng on the time of day and/or day of week,

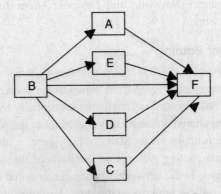

Fig. 4.7. Time-dependent routing, TDR

as in Table 4.2. A weekday, for example, can be divided into different time periods, with each time period resulting in different route patterns being defined to route traffic streams between the same pair of exchanges. For instance in Table 4.2, in *time* 1, calls originating from exchange B to destination F can be routed via BF, BCF, and BDF; and for *time* 2 via BF, BAF, and BEF.

Table 4.2. Time-dependent routing (TDR) table

Time period	B to F route pattern
1.	BF, BCF, BDF
2.	BF, BAF, BEF

Time dependent routing takes advantage of idle circuit capacity in other possible routes between the originating and terminating exchanges, which may exist due to non-coincident busy periods. Crankback may be utilized to identify downstream blocking on the second link of each two-link alternative path [E.170].

Dynamic Non-Hierarchical Routing (DNHR) is an example of TDR schemes, which was used by the USA AT&T FTS-2000 Network till 2002 when it was replaced by *Real-Time Network Routing* (RTNR)—a state-dependent routing (SDR) scheme.

4.2.6 General Comments on Routing

The routing schemes addressed in the previous subsections can relate to automatic and semi-automatic telephone traffic from fixed and mobile (both land and maritime) stations. Each routing scheme allows its primary objective to be achieved with maximum economy by the most efficient use of costly circuits and switching centres while safeguarding the grade of service (GoS) and quality of transmission. The rules governing the routing-types address connections consisting of a number of circuits in tandem. In practice, though, the large majority of international telephone traffic is routed on direct circuits (*i.e.*, no intermediate switching point) between International Switching Centres (ISCs). Much of the techniques utilised for these routing schemes for circuit-switched networks have been extended to packet-based networks.

Current and future networks are rapidly evolving to carry a multitude of voice/ISDN services and packet data services on *internet protocol* (IP)-based networks, driven in part by the rapidly growing IP-based data services. In this context, routing is playing an essential role for meeting the QoS constraints that are inherent to the various services. As such, the scope of routing dynamism would include the establishment of connections for narrowband, wideband, and broadband multimedia services within multiservice networks and between multiservice networks. A multiservice network refers to one in which various classes of service share the transmission, switching, management, and other resources of the network. It is envisaged that various classes of service will still meet the quantitative performance requirements, such as end-to-end blocking, delay, and/or delay-jitter objectives. These performance requirements are likely to be achieved through a combination of dynamic routing, traffic management, and capacity management.

4.3 CONTROL OF ROUTING

To control the connection or bearer-path routing throughout a network that may be automatically controlled by the switching equipment, certain conditions must be met:

(*a*) At each switching centre encountered in setting up a call, early-choice routes are tested in order for a free outlet, with the call eventually being offered to the final route if a free outlet is not found on one of the direct routes.

(b) Calls originating in one final route chain and switched to another are then only switched to exchanges of lower classification in that chain: not switched to centres of higher classification, or to a third chain.

These conditions would ensure that:

o calls cannot be routed over one link more than once during the establishment of a connection;

o the maximum number of links assigned during design is not exceeded; and

o the transmission loss assigned to early-choice circuits does not exceed the maximum permitted within the limits set by the transmission plan.

4.4 SUMMARY

Routing involves the selection of a path from the originating node to the destination node in a network. This chapter has discussed routing selection methods, which are categorized into the following four types: fixed routing (FR), time-dependent routing (TDR), state-dependent routing (SDR), and event-dependent routing (EDR). These methods are associated with routing tables, which consist of a route and rules to select one path from the route for a given connection or bandwidth-allocation request.

The advent of smart digital switches in the network has allowed the evolution of traffic routing from fixed hierarchical to dynamic non-hierarchical.

Routing strategies relate to those that involve overflow having direct first-choice (high-usage) routes, and that involve indirect alternative routes. In a situation of traffic overload, the proportion of alternatively routed traffic would increase rapidly with the risk of severe degradation of network performance.

QUESTIONS

1. What is routing, and what are its possible goals?
2. What are the two major requirements for network architecture's routing strategy?
3. Describe the basic differences between circuit-switched and packet-switched routing.
4. Discuss the performance criteria employed for route selection.
5. Explain the difference between static and alternate routing in a circuit-switching network.
6. Describe briefly the following concepts related to circuit-switched networks: fixed hierarchical routing, adaptive routing, and crankback.
7. Describe the principle and the algorithm of fixed hierarchical routing.
8. Describe the operating principle of alternative routing. Use an example. What does an optimal route mean?
9. The nodes A, B, C and D form a completely looped network. Node E connects to A and C. Describe, from the user's point of view, optimal routing from B to D using the augmented routing tree.
10. Explain the principle of adaptive routing.
11. Describe the routing principle of the long-distance network of Nigeria or your country.

5

SIGNALLING

The signalling system used in telecommunication networks has evolved over time with advances in technology: from the analogue to digital although analogue telephones are still in use in many countries. The signalling strategy applied depends on whether the line signals are for controlling the seizure and supervision of inter-exchange circuits, or for call establishment. With technology comes the various switching systems; thus presenting the network planners, or network administration, the task of appropriating relevant signalling systems and protocols for the various switching technologies and components to interwork between them. The signalling protocol defines a standard set of information elements and a method of transport ensuring network components interoperate.

This chapter explores the concept of signalling as applied to public telephone network.

5.1 SIGNALLING: WHAT IS IT?

Simply, signalling is the sending of a signal from one end of a circuit to the other end of the circuit informing a user or subscriber that a message is to be sent. In a general form, signalling refers to the exchange of information between call components required to provide and maintain telecommunication services. Signalling provides the ability to transfer information within networks, between different networks, and between subscribers.

The information the signalling system is required to transmit varies proportionately with the size and complexity of the network as well as the facilities the network is required to provide both at present and in future. For example the signalling requirements of earliest networks, which consisted of a number of manual exchanges, are clearly different from those of a large automatic national network providing a wide range of facilities. Some of these manual exchanges may still be in service in some countries.

Ideally, a single signalling system is required throughout the entire network as this avoids the need for conversion of equipment that is required at the points where different systems interface. In practice, this is almost impossible to achieve due to the residue of signalling systems from earlier phases of the evolution of the network. Aside, administrations (could indicate both a public telecommunication administration and a recognized private operating agency) usually adopt a signalling that is not entirely uniform but is composed of several similar systems with as many common characteristics as possible, so that interface problems are kept to a minimum.

The variation in types of transmission links also results in different types of signalling being required for different parts of the network. For example, *direct current* signalling is used on the subscribers line that is metallic but this is impossible on a radio system. The more information that has to be signalled and interfaces that are to be traversed, the longer the delay in transmitting the information. Thus extends the post dialing delay experienced by the customer and tends to increase the quantity of network plant required.

In practice, signalling is either end-to-end or link-to-link. In the end-to-end signalling, information is sent directly from the point of origin to the destination point. It may traverse intermediate points but does not interact with them. Link-to-link signalling is a process where signalling is passed from one node to the next with the call being established or cleared on a link-by-link basis. Often, link-to-link signalling is received and transmitted at each transit point. Usually a compromise between the two systems is adopted. A common choice is for link-to-link signalling to be used for line signals, (those used to supervise individual circuits), and end-to-end signalling for information signals, (those which transmit the information needed to establish the call). Regardless of the signalling type employed, it is therefore advantageous to select systems that signal at high speed.

In essence, signalling is a major component of any telephone system: it refers to the exchange of information between call components required to provide and maintain service. For example electric pulses or audible tones are used for alerting (requesting service), for addressing (e.g., dialing the called party's number at the subscriber set), for supervision (monitoring idle lines), and for information (providing dial tones, busy signals, and recordings—accessing a voice mailbox, sending a call-waiting tone). As users of the public telephone network, we exchange signalling with network elements all the time. A lot of descriptive information about the various signals from and to the public telephone networks can be written. However, the major signalling facilities for the public telephone networks are discussed in this chapter.

5.1.1 Basic Signalling Architecture

Figure 5.1 shows a basic signalling architecture. Signalling to the rest of the world is sent out over the signalling links through the switching centres (e.g., A, E, W)—which could be primary, tertiary, main exchanges or several exchanges in tandem-and other minor exchanges (e.g., B, C, D, X, Y, Z). Often in the literature, the exchanges are considered registers and the signalling between these exchanges is called interregister signalling. Interregister signalling uses forward and backward in-band multifrequency signals in each timeslot to transfer called and calling party numbers, as well as the calling party category.

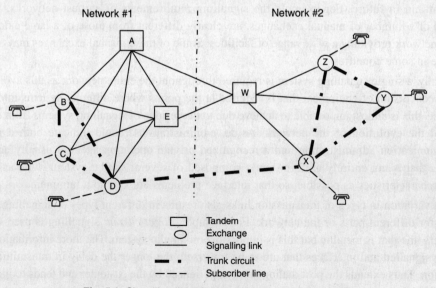

Fig. 5.1. Signalling links for two interconnected networks

There may be several signalling systems used in a functional public telephone network, and there may be country-specific variations. The signalling system in the Australian network has used a link-by-link basis for the line signals controlling the seizure and supervision of inter-exchange circuits. The transfer of all other information needed to establish the call has been on a generally end-to-end basis using *multifrequency-code compelled-sequence* information signalling system or decadic pulsing where step-by-step equipment was involved.

Line signalling, for example, is used to allow the near and far end to know the state of a particular call and could be segmented as follows: loop-disconnect signalling on direct current (DC) circuits; loop sequential or pulse signalling on standard carrier circuits with or without out-of-band signalling facilities; or simply *multifrequency-compelled* (MFC) signalling on the links throughout the network. Signalling on subscribers' lines may be different from those inter-switch links; in that case, DC signalling potentials may be appropriate. DC signalling is a relic of the old manual systems employed as a method of interconnecting switchboards. These aforelisted signalling types are called *Channel Associated Signalling* (CAS). Another signalling approach, called the *Common Channel Signalling* (CCS), is where all the signalling information is concentrated in a single dedicated channel. Signalling System Number 7 (SS_7, or C_7) is an example of a CCS system. The basic principles of each signalling type are discussed next under appropriate headings.

5.1.2   Channel Associated Signalling

In *Channel Associated Signalling* (CAS), the signalling information is carried down the same physical channel as the circuit traffic. Although a channel is allocated to each circuit-traffic, no channel is particularly dedicated to signalling. CAS is also referred to as 'robbed bit signalling' because the least significant bit of information in a DS0 carried on the T_1 signal is "robbed or stolen" from the channels that carry voice, for example, which is then used to transmit framing and clocking information. This process is sometimes called *in-band signalling*.

Unlike the T_1 systems, E_1 systems transparently pass all 8 bits of every sample. Most telephone systems outside North America use the E_1 systems. In the E_1 systems, a channel outside the nominated traffic channel, sometimes called *out-of-band* channel, carries the signalling information. Classification of signal levels (DS_i, where $i = 0, 1, 2, ...$) and channel capacity for each carrier system can be seen in chapter 3, section 3.1. Typical examples of CAS systems are loop disconnect, multi-frequency compelled (MFC) regional signalling system number 2 (MFC/R_2) access dialling. Each of these systems is discussed in the next subsections, with the exception of Regional Signalling System No. 2 (also called Signalling System R_2 or simply R_2—formerly called the MFC Bern System, which is common to E_1 networks). Unfortunately, there is no single signalling standard for R_2, although various aspects of the ITU-T recommendations, namely Q.400 through to Q.490, define R_2, but a number of countries and geographic regions implement R_2 in entirely different ways.

Each T_1 channel carries a sequence of frames. Each frame consists of 24 channels (virtual DS0s) and carries 8 data bits plus a bit designated as the framing bit, as seen in Fig. 5.2(a). This makes a total of 193 bits per frame. T_1 frames are sent at 8 kHz. The first vertical row of 8 bits of Fig. 5.2(a) is sent first, followed by the second, and on down the line. After the last set of 8 bits is sent, a single framing bit follows, and then comes the next frame.

A dozen frames make up a *superframe* (SF). A superframe designates the framing bits of the even numbered frames as signalling bits. The framing bits line up in a particular pattern like

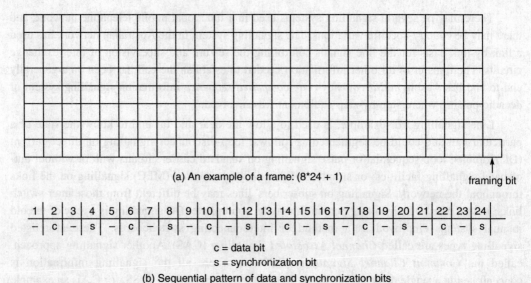

(a) An example of a frame: (8*24 + 1)   framing bit

1	2	3	4	5	6	7	8	9	10	11	12	13	14	15	16	17	18	19	20	21	22	23	24
–	c	–	s	–	c	–	s	–	c	–	s	–	c	–	s	–	c	–	s	–	c	–	s

c = data bit
s = synchronization bit

(b) Sequential pattern of data and synchronization bits

Fig. 5.2. Superframe arrangement

100011011100. This pattern serves to discern which 8 bits belong to which channel or circuit. This discerning is known as *frame synchronization*. CAS looks specifically at every sixth frame for the channel's associated signalling information. These bits are commonly referred to as A- and B-bits.

An *extended superframe* (ESF) has twice the size of an ordinary superframe, and provides continuous error checking and a separate data channel. Every fourth bit provides its framing synchronization. ESF has four signalling bits per channel or timeslot occurring in frames 6, 12, 18, and 24, which are called the A-, B-, C-, and D-bits respectively. ESF provides 16 signalling states in the 193rd bit to ensure adequate synchronization, supervisory control, and maintenance capabilities.

5.1.2.1 *Multifrequency-Compelled Signalling*

The multi-frequency compelled signalling system (MFC/R_2) is a telephony signalling protocol originally used to provide switch to switch (or register to register) signalling over analogue copper pair wiring at a higher speed than had been possible with pulse dialling. It was once considered an obsolete signalling concept; digital MFC/R_2 over E_1 trunks is still heavily used in many countries. MFC/R_2 offers an extensive set of signals describing the status and category of the *calling* and *called* parties. This inter-register signalling is generally performed end-to-end by a *compelled* procedure, meaning that a tone in one direction is acknowledged by a tone in the other direction. This mode of signalling is known as *multifrequency compelled* (MFC) signalling.

MFC/R_2, rather than being the relic of the past, Iridium satellite system connects its communication system to the terrestrial networks through gateways, which transfer traffic to public switched (circuit) telephone network (PSTN) through pulse code modulation (PCM) transmission and integrated services digital network (ISDN) multifrequency compelled signalling.

In principle, the MFC/R_2 system consists of 2 sets of 6 frequencies f_i (where $i = 0, 1, ..., 5$), which can be grouped in combinations of 2 to provide 15 *forward* and 15 backward codes, as seen in Table 5.1—derived from Nortel Networks (2000). Not all signals may be in use. The number of possible frequency combinations depends on the assigned, standard frequencies pertaining to systems being used.

Table 5.1: MFC frequency combinations

Combination number	Frequencies, f_i
1	$f_0 + f_1$
2	$f_0 + f_2$
3	$f_1 + f_2$
4	$f_0 + f_3$
5	$f_1 + f_3$
6	$f_2 + f_3$
7	$f_0 + f_4$
8	$f_1 + f_4$
9	$f_2 + f_4$
10	$f_3 + f_4$
11	$f_0 + f_5$
12	$f_1 + f_5$
13	$f_2 + f_5$
14	$f_3 + f_5$
15	$f_4 + f_5$

The forward signals consist of signals transmitted from the originating end to the terminating end. There are two groups:

o Group I "Forward" signals are dialled address digits which identify the called party.

o Group II "Forward" signals identify the category of the calling party (e.g., Restricted Station).

The backward signals consist of signals transmitted from the terminating end to the originating end. There are two groups:

o Group A "Backward" signals are the response to the Group I "Forward" signals.

o Group B "Backward" signals identify the status of the called party (*e.g.*, Station Busy).

MFC signals are sent over the regular talking channels and are transmitted as readily as speech. Each *Forward Signal* sent on a trunk is steadily maintained until acknowledged by a *Backward Signal*. When the *Backward Signal* is received, the *Forward Signal* is removed which in turn forces the *Backward Signal* to be removed as well. This "compelled" sequence is repeated until the protocol is complete and the call is established. Backward signals can also be sent in pulse form without the prior reception of a Forward signal.

Most fixed-line modern phones use *dual tone multifrequency* (DTMF—the generic term for touch-tone, or tone dialling, *e.g.*, Fig. 5.3) rather than pulse dialing, but most telephone equipment retains support for pulse dialling for backward compatibility. Also, some models of keypad phones also have a tone/pulse switch which can be toggled to switch between the two making these phones usable in areas where DTMF dialling is not accepted, *e.g.*, in most of Eastern Bloc countries. More is said about the operation of DTMF in the next subsection 5.1.2.1.1.

Variation to R_2 signalling has resulted in limited use of frequencies from optimally assigned frequencies. For example, in R_2 signalling that uses only five of the six frequencies are known as

Fig. 5.3. A multifrequency dialling telephone with recall button

decadic pulsing (loop-disconnect signalling) systems, or decadic-CAS systems. Decadic or dial pulsing is defined as a momentary on-hook condition that causes loop making and breaking in the local loop and there must be an inter-digit pause (or period) between two consecutive train of pulses. Decadic register signalling causes one of the line signalling bits to temporarily change pulse (or state) a number of times to represent a particular digit. This toggling is similar to loop disconnect dialling. In *decadic pulsing*, a digit having a value of n is represented by $n + 1$ pulses.

It is possible that terminal equipment provided with a loop disconnect signalling facility may be subject to appropriate national regulations in respect to such facility. It is advisable that the reader is conversant with the national regulations in order to be connected to his/her public telephone network (*e.g.*, PSTN).

Decadic dialling is inherently slower than tone based (DTMF and MFC) dialling and is, therefore, encountered less often.

5.1.2.1.1   Off-hook/On-hook signalling

For completeness, the functions of *off-hook* (*i.e.*, open loop-state) and on-hook (*i.e.*, closed loop-state) signalling are briefly discussed. The loop-state (open or closed) is determined by the instant state of the loop resistance. When the exchange detects a closure, the loop resistance becomes lower than 2 kΩ. An opening is detected when the loop resistance becomes higher than 15 kΩ.

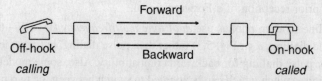

Fig. 5.4. Multifrequency-compelled end-to-end signalling procedure

As seen in Fig. 5.4 when a subscriber wishes to make a call, the telephone handset is lifted and an *off-hook signal* (also called *seize signal* or *calling signal*) is enabled which informs the exchange that there is a call request. Upon receiving an off-hook signal by the exchange, the control system:

o allocates some common equipment to the call and connects the necessary path;

o reserves some dual tone (or multifrequency) receivers to receive the dialled digits from a compatible tone telephone set. The dialled digits are also called the address digits, the address signal, or the register signal. Either the *dual-tone multifrequency* (DTMF) signalling or the decadic pulse signalling may be used for the address signal; and

o connects the dial tone to the calling subscriber to signal the ready state of receiving dialled digits.

The calling subscriber dials the called subscriber numbers after receiving the dial tone. When one presses the telephone keypad, two specific voice band frequencies: one from a group of four low frequencies and the other from a group of four higher frequencies, are sent to the telephone exchange—typical frequencies are listed in Table 5.2.

Table 5.2. DTMF standard signal frequency pairs

Button digit or designation	Frequency bands (Hz)	
	Low band	High band
1	697	1209
2	697	1336
3	697	1477
4	770	1209
5	770	1336
6	770	1477
7	852	1209
8	852	1336
9	852	1336
0	941	1209
*	941	1336
#	941	1477
A [FO (Flash override)]	697	1633
B [F (Flash)]	770	1663
C [I (Immediate)]	852	1633
D [P (Priority)]	941	1633

The tone frequencies are designed to avoid harmonics and other problems that could arise when two tones are sent and received. Accurate transmission from the subscriber's phone and accurate decoding at the telephone exchange end is important. Each of the 12 keypads corresponds to a different pair of frequencies. The telephone exchange can then listen and decode the tone to determine which keys are pressed, enabling dialling. Using Table 5.2 and Fig. 5.5 as a reference, if the digit 1 on the keypad is pressed, for example, the tones 1209 Hz and 697 Hz are generated. There are extra four buttons—A, B, C, D—hidden on subscriber telephones: they are special buttons employed for communications signalling. The tones are the same at higher band frequencies but varied in the lower band. The extra codes (A, B, C, D) are very useful in preventing standard telephone codes from being used to control remote devices, and these extra codes can give you override status when used correctly in a two-way radio system.

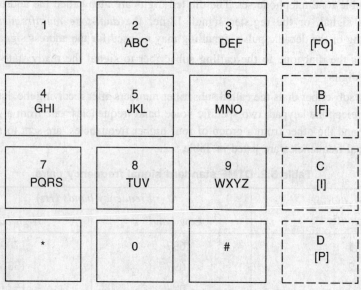

Note: [ ] = Defence keypad

Fig. 5.5. DTMF dialling pushbutton-arrangement for public and defence telephones

Tactical telephones have 16 keys; the same 12 keypads as those used by the public exchange carriers with the precedence: extra unhidden four buttons namely FO, F, I, and P, which are respectively Flash Override, Flash, Immediate, and Priority. The precedence represents priority levels that could establish a phone connection with varying degrees of immediacy, killing other conversations on the network if necessary with FO being the greatest priority, down to P being of lesser priority. The keypads frequency-pairs are similar to the public telephones, except for added line security.

The major advantage of the DTMF is the speed; typical duration of a digit is 50 ms, with a minimum inter-digit period of 45 ms. The biggest disadvantage of CAS signalling is its use of user bandwidth in order to perform signalling functions. CAS systems tend to be slow and provide a very limited capability to transfer information between the service users.

5.1.3 Common Channel Signalling

In *Common Channel Signalling* (CCS), the signalling information is concentrated in a single dedicated channel, such that all of the signalling information for many voice channels in a telephony system can be conveyed over a single channel dedicated to signalling. An example of CCS is the Signalling System Number 7 (SS_7)—also called CCS_7 (Common Channel Signalling System 7), C_7, Number 7, and $CCIS_7$ (Common Channel Interoffice Signalling 7). SS_7 signalling is done *out-of-band*, meaning that SS_7 signalling messages are transported over a separate data connection; thus representing a significant security improvement over earlier systems that used *in-band* signalling. SS_7 network is a very important component in the public telephone networks used to route signalling traffic, carrying all the signalling messages necessary to set up calls, break down calls, or provide extra telephony services. Simply, SS_7 provides the means for all the nodes within the network to communicate and coordinate and make the necessary voice circuit connections to provide users with seamless service. Also, SS$_7$ controls the network in the manner in which traffic is routed from one location to another. The specifications for SS$_7$ are in the ITU-T Recommendations: Q.700 through to Q.716.

5.1.3.1 *SS$_7$ Signalling Architecture*

The basic SS$_7$ network architecture consists of three essential signalling components or points interconnected through signalling links, as shown in Fig. 5.6. The three signalling components are:

o *Signal switching point or service switching point* (SSP);

o *Signal control point or service control point* (SCP); and

o *Signal transfer point or service transfer point* (STP).

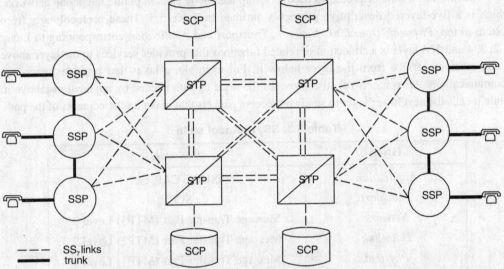

Fig. 5.6. SS$_7$ network architecture

In the SS$_7$ network, each signalling point is uniquely identified by a numeric point code. Point codes are carried in signalling messages exchanged between signalling points to identify the source and destination of each message. Each signalling point uses a routing table to select an appropriate signalling path for each message. A brief discussion of the signalling points follows under appropriate subheadings.

5.1.3.1.1 Signal Switching Point

The *Signal switching point or service switching point* (SSP) is the local exchange in the public telephone network that carries the telephone conversations. An SSP can be a combination of voice switch and SS$_7$ switch, or an adjunct computer system (front end) connected to the local exchange's voice switch. With advances in technology, the traffic mix found in the SS$_7$ networks has changed significantly; it has become a mixture of circuit-related and packet-related messages. In fact, computers adjunct to existing switches are performing many SSP functions in the transmission of specific SS$_7$ messages across the public telephone network.

An SSP uses the calling party information in the setup message, which is then converted into SS$_7$ signalling message to route or connect the information from one exchange to another; typically an exchange with a direct connection to it. For example, the SSP uses the information provided by the calling party (*e.g.*, the subscriber's telephone number—dialled digits) and then determines how to connect or route the call. The routing table will identify which trunk circuit to use to connect the call, and which exchange the trunk will terminate at. The SS_7 message is then sent to the adjacent exchange requesting a circuit connection on the specified trunk. When the adjacent exchange grants permission to connect this trunk, it sends an acknowledgement message back to the originating exchange. Using the called party information in the setup message, the adjacent exchange can determine how to connect the call to its final destination. Of course, this source-to-destination process may require several trunk connections between several adjacent exchanges, which the SSP will manage until the final destination is reached.

5.1.3.1.1.1 *SSP Protocol Suite*

The SSP has a suite of protocols used to set up telephone calls in public telephone networks, which is a five-layered descriptive protocols outlined in Table 5.3. These protocols are, from bottom to top, *Physical*, *Data Link*, *Network*, *Transport* and *Application* corresponding to Layer 1, 2, 3, 4 and 5. A layer is a collection of related functions that provides services to the layer above it and receives service from the layer below it. For example, a layer that provides error-free communications across a network also provides the route or path needed by applications above it, while it calls the next lower layer to send and receive packets that make up the contents of the path.

Table 5.3. SS_7 protocol suite

Layer	Protocols
Application	ISUP, TCAP, etc.
Transport	SCCP
Network	Message Transfer Part (MTP3) Level 3
Data link	Message Transfer Part (MTP2) Level 2
Physical	Message Transfer Part (MTP1) Level 1

The *application layer* (Level 5) provides semantic conversion between associated application processes. For example, when a call is set up from one subscriber to another, many exchanges may be involved, possibly across international boundaries. The *ISDN User Part* (ISUP) allows telephone calls to be set up correctly, using the relevant switches signal call-related information (*e.g.*, calling or called party number) to the next switch in the network. The ISUP is part of the SS_7, specified as part of the ITU-T Recommendations [Q.76], as well as in the American National Standards Institute (ANSI, T1.113-YEAR).

The *transport layer* (Level 4) responds to service requests from the *application layer*. Typically, processors in the host computer operational system, not routers or switches, handle the transport layer. The Signalling Connection Control Part (SCCP), a routing protocol in SS_7 protocol suite, provides end-to-end routing for *transaction capabilities application part* (TCAP) messages to their proper database.

TCAP (*transaction capabilities application part*) protocol enables the deployment of advanced intelligent network services by supporting non-circuit related information exchange between signalling points using the SCCP connectionless service. Also, TCAP supports remote control; that is, the ability to invoke features in another remote network switch. It will be discussed in chapter 8 the mobile communications principle, but the involvement of TCAP in service profile of a mobile system is explained, thus. When a mobile-phone subscriber roams into a new *mobile switching center* (MSC) area, the integrated *visitor location register* (VLR) requests service profile information from the subscriber's *home location register* (HLR) using *mobile application part* (MAP) information carried within TCAP messages. More is said about these registers in chapter 8. TCAP messages are contained within the SCCP portion of a *message signal unit* (MSU).

An MSU provides the structure to carry the information messages in the SS_7 network. These information messages being transmitted in the SS_7 network can be circuit-and non-circuit based messages. Non-circuit based messages refer to the queries for additional routing information and network management data. MSUs originate from MTP_3 or from an MTP_3 user. MSU serves as payload-carrier for higher-level messages such as SCCP, ISUP, and TCAP. In essence, helping to transfer user messages between two peer Level 4 protocols in signalling points.

SCCP (Signalling Connection Control Part), a routing protocol in SS_7 protocol suite in Level 4, provides end-to-end routing for TCAP messages to their proper database. Functionally, SCCP

- o Provides connectionless and connection-oriented network services above *network layer*.
- o Provides subsystem numbers to allow messages to be addressed to specific applications or subsystems at the signalling points.
- o Serves as the transport layer for TCAP-based services such as free-phone or free-call (*e.g.*, USA 800/888, Australia 1800), calling card, local number portability, and wireless roaming.
- o Provides the means by which an STP can perform *global title translation* (GTT)—a procedure by which the destination signalling point, and subsystem number (SSN), is determined from global numbers or digits present in the signalling message. The global title digits may be any sequence of digits pertinent to the service requested.

For MTP users, SCCP messages are composed of three parts:

- o A *mandatory fixed part* that contains all parameters that must be present in the message. These parameters are of a fixed length with no need for length indicator.
- o A *mandatory variable part* contains all parameters that must be present in the message. These parameters are of variable lengths requiring length indicators. Each length indicator precedes each parameter. No parameter tagging is required to state the parameter types because the parameter types and their order is explicitly defined in the SCCP message type.
- o An *optional part* consists of those parameters that are not always necessary. A parameter name and a length indicator precede each parameter. Because the parameter types and their order are unknown, parameter name is required for each parameter type. Typically, parameter name has one-octet field pattern.

SCCP message formats are not universally uniform: there are differences in that defined by ANSI and other defined by ITU-T. The reader is advised to verify the appropriate format relevant to the network system operating in your country.

The *message transfer part* (MTP), the lower portions of the SS_7 protocol suite, comprises of *data link layer*, *network layer* and *physical layer*. These layers are part of the *Open Systems Interconnection* (OSI) model. The reader who desires a deeper knowledge of the architecture of an OSI model is referred to the author's Satellite Communication Engineering (Marcel Dekker, 2002).

The MTP is designed as a joint transport system for the messages of different users. The requirements of the different users, which are not necessarily the same and may differ in importance and stringency, have to be met by the MTP. The MTP, whilst meeting these requirements in relation to the telephone and data transmission services, the signalling network management component must meet the current and those of future users. In the light of this consideration, three layers performing different functions enabling overall signalling system performance to be achieved are discussed, as follows.

The *network layer* (abbreviated to MTP$_3$) performs routing functions, and provides the functional and procedural means of transporting signalling messages through the SS7 network from their source to the requested endpoints. Each network element in the SS7 network has a unique point-code or address that allows message routing to be performed. This layer is also responsible for network management: for example, when situation in the *data link* layer changes, the MTP$_3$ responds accordingly by establishing alternative links and propagates information about route availability through the network. Routers operate at this layer sending data throughout the extended network and making the Internet possible.

The *data link layer* (abbreviated to MTP$_2$) provides the functional and procedural means for transferring data between network entities. It also detects and corrects errors that may occur in the Physical layer. Whenever SS$_7$ message sequence is checked and found incorrect, MTP$_2$ retransmits unacknowledged messages using *signal units* (also called packets).

The *physical layer* (abbreviated to MTP$_1$), the most basic network layer, defines all the electrical and physical specifications for devices particularly the relationship between a device and a physical medium. MTP1 provides the means of transmitting raw bits rather than packets over a physical *data link* connecting the network nodes; it simply performs services that are requested by the *data link layer*. Typically, MTP$_1$ uses a timeslot in a T-/E-carrier.

In essence, the Message Transfer Part (MTP) of the Signalling System No. 7 (SS$_7$) is designed as a joint transport system for the messages of different users responsible for reliable, unduplicated and in-sequence transport of messages between communication partners. Different countries use different variants of the MTP protocols. For correct implementation of the MTP protocol, the reader should consult ITU-T Recommendations Q.701, Q.704 and Q.705, and in Q.706 for signalling network management in case of failures and traffic congestion.

5.1.3.1.2 Signal Control Point

Signal or Service Control Point (SCP) houses the service logic and provides service control. The SCP communicates directly with the switch and intercepts triggers and other service-related messages from the Service Switching Point (SSP). These messages are often routed to the SCP through a Signal Transfer Point (STP), which provides routing of the SS$_7$ messages within the network. The SCP acts as the gateway between the core SS$_7$ and the world of the Intelligent Peripheral (IP). The Intelligent Peripheral contains the content and helps the SCP decide how to deliver the enhanced services to the subscriber. The interconnection between the SCP and the Intelligent Peripheral is sometimes Internet-based. Thus, the SCP lives in both worlds—the service provider's SS$_7$ space and the Internet space. It heralds the approach of next-generation networks (NGN), which blend the public switched (circuit) telephone network (PSTN) and the public switched data network (PSDN). The SCP databases provide static information (*e.g.*, the services a subscriber has signed up for) and dynamic information (*e.g.*, the ever-changing traffic conditions in the network). Given that the signalling network is separate, a voice circuit is not tied up until a connection is made between the calling and called parties.

New SS$_7$ Intelligent Peripherals are increasingly being added to the public telephone network to provide key functions in enhanced services, such as customized voice announcements and voice recognition in order to meet the wireless customer demands particularly personalization—meaning anytime, anywhere access; and multimedia person-to-person messaging. Critical to the implementation of these enhanced mobile services is the SCP.

5.1.3.1.3 Signal Transfer Point

The signal transfer points (STPs) are the most versatile of all the SS$_7$ entities: they are packet switches; act like routers in the SS$_7$ network; and can act like a firewall, screening messages to and from, and with, other networks. An STP does not usually originate messages but routes SS$_7$ messages (based on information contained in the message format) to outgoing signalling links over the SS$_7$ network. STPs are a major component in the network.

5.1.3.1.4 SS$_7$ Network Survivability

As discussed in chapter 2, section 2.6.3, subscribers' demands from a network must be satisfied even under the risk of link or node disruption. In practice, since the SS7 network is critical to call processing, SCPs and STPs are usually deployed in mated-pair configurations in separate physical locations to ensure network-wide service in the event of an isolated failure. Links between signalling points are also provisioned in pairs. Traffic is shared across all links in the linkset. If one of the links fails, the signalling traffic is rerouted over another link in the linkset. Thus, the SS$_7$ protocol provides both error correction and retransmission capabilities allowing continued service in the event of a signalling link or point failures.

5.1.3.1.5 SS$_7$ Summary

SS$_7$ identifies both functions to be performed by a signalling-system network and a protocol to enable their performance. The SS$_7$ network acts as the backbone for the Advanced Intelligent Network (AIN), provides access to AIN features, allows for efficient call setup and teardown and interconnects a myriad of telecommunications providers under a common signalling network. SS$_7$ is widely used in many countries around the world including Australia, Canada, UK, USA, etc.

5.2 WHAT TO CONSIDER WHEN SELECTING A SIGNALLING SYSTEM

Many factors influence the selection of a given signalling system for a particular application; for example, satellite systems because of long round-trip propagation delays, echo suppressor insertion in international trunks and satellite links, or where compatibility of speech interpolation systems to signalling systems are concerned. The overarching concern is what the network designers/administrators decide upon, and what, where, and when to specify the requirements to be met by the signalling system. In an attempt to understand the factors that should be considered, some questions are drawn up which may serve as a guideline [Q.7]:

1. Does the transmission system provide for sufficient bandwidth (*e.g.*, for outband line signalling)?
2. Is the signal capacity sufficient to allow the setting-up of an ordinary connection?
3. Is an additional exchange of information required, *e.g.*:
   - for echo suppressor control,

- to increase routing facilities,
- to obtain or to offer detailed information on congestion,
- to obtain or to offer information on the condition of the called subscriber line,
- to obtain or to offer information on the nature of the call for identification, or for management purposes?

4. What requirements have to be set for the speed of the signalling system? What post-dialling and answering delays are to be tolerated?

5. Is there any interdependence between the minimum bundle size and signalling (*e.g.*, as in the case of pilot interruption control of Signalling System R_2)?

6. In the case of satellite systems, does the earth station require an extra interface between the terrestrial access circuits and the satellite links, and the effect of inclusion of one satellite link in terms of long round-trip propagation delays (about 540 ± 40 ms) on a telephone connection and subscribers conversation?

7. If use is made of two satellite links in tandem, what arrangement is made with the subsequent transit centres?

8. Is it necessary to introduce a new signalling system?

9. Is the signalling system suitable for application to the particular exchange type, *e.g.*, electromechanical exchanges?

10. In the case of a transmission system with speech interpolation, what effort in place ensuring that the signalling system to be used is compatible with speech interpolation?

To ensure compatibility of the signalling systems used for international automatic and semiautomatic telephone networking it is necessary to keep to a minimum the number of different types of equipment serving the various routes at any one exchange. Ensuring this compatibility requires an understanding of certain factors, which have been discussed in this section.

5.3 SUMMARY

In this chapter, the objective of signalling in public telephone networks was explained. . Signalling provides the ability to transfer information within networks, between different networks, and between subscribers. Also discussed are the two types of signalling namely: channel associated signalling (CAS) and common channel signalling (CCS), as well as their management and relevant governing standards.

QUESTIONS

1. Explain the function of the signalling network nodes.

2. How is the signalling information carried in digital signalling 1 (DS_1) and what is the bandwidth of the media? (Pointer: see also Chapter 3, section 3.2.)

3. What protocol does MTP user-channel use on the data link layer?

4. What are the signalling issues to be considered when planning national and/or international links?

6

SWITCHING

With digital switching now a mature technology in circuit-switched telecommunications networks, this chapter examines the principles of switching matrix, as well as *space* and *time* switching architectures and associated switching fabrics.

6.1 OVERVIEW

Public telephone networks use switching systems to connect and disconnect subscribers by activating and deactivating switching devices. Historically, switches are analogues, mechanically moving contacts that connect a pair of wires, or closing the selected contacts in relays providing connection of two telephones. Switches have migrated from electromechanical switching systems to microprocessors controlled switching systems (called the *digital data exchange*, DDEX), which allow subscribers to simultaneously interface with the network.

The microprocessors controlled switching system contains special separate memory with special *direct memory access* (DMA) modules. DMA is a separate peripheral module that performs *Input/Output* (I/O) transfers between channels. A basic DMA structure is shown in Fig. 6.1. The DMA module generates a sequence of addresses and autonomously reads/writes RAM memory data, independent of the *central processing unit* (CPU). DMA has same clock input as CPU. Data is transferred in blocks. Data bytes go to and from consecutive RAM addresses. When block transfer is complete, DMA causes a CPU interrupt. CPU module performs data manipulation and logical operations using CPU registers as source(s) and destination(s) of data. The *random access*

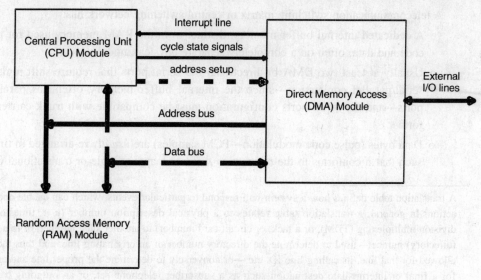

Fig. 6.1. A DMA channel structure

memory (RAM), the data storage module, reads the operational code from processor's memory, and reads/writes data from/to data RAM addresses.

Some designs may use many devices to connect to the bus. In such a situation, the control signals (not shown in Fig 6.1) would determine which device is the destination of the current bus data values. Some designs may use the main address bus to transfer initial DMA start/stop address settings. If a *connection memory* (CM) module is added to the DMA structure (as shown in Fig 6.2) to map time sequence of I/O timeslots, then the DMA channel structure will be similar to a digital telecommunications switching matrix where the CM may contain one type of translation table[1] or indirect address table for mapping input time slots to output time slots. The data output of this CM is used as an address to access the buffer RAM. The CPU can change the content of the CM.

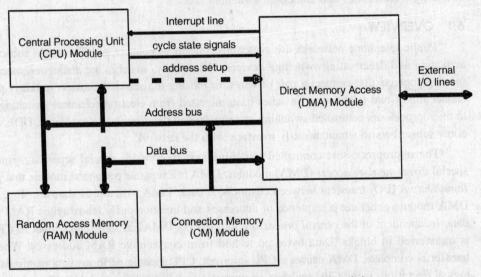

Fig. 6.2. A DMA channel structure as a digital switch

A telecommunication switching matrix or central switching network has:

o A dedicated internal buffer memory, distinct from the RAM memory used for program code and data; often on a completely separate physical module.

o Usually at least two DMA bi-directional I/O serial ports that require shift registers for serial/parallel conversion—since the internal buffer memory often has parallel data ports—and the serial ports configuration must be compatible with trunk carrier-stream format.

o Data bytes (pulse code modulation—PCM samples) are *usually* re-arranged in time order such that it conforms to the *connection memory*-mapping table or translational format.

---

[1] A translation table defines how a system will respond to particular events, which can enable one or more actions. In general, a translation table relates to a physical description number (*e.g.*, timeslot in time division multiplexing (TDM), or a rack, or circuit card number) to another such number, or to a symbolic (directory) number—used to determine the directory number of an originating line, and thus the features allowed for that line, its calling line ID, etc.—or conversely to determine the proper line and/or timeslot for a final or intermediate destination such as a subscriber telephone set, or an outgoing trunk in an originating or transit switch.

In terms of diagrammatic notations, the next sections gain from Karnaugh (1974).

6.2 SWITCHING FUNCTIONAL ELEMENTS

Switching is used to share the capacity of a communications channel between several users, just as abstractions like 'processes' are used to share CPU and memory in multitasking operating systems. The simplest switching structure is a square (or rectangular) array of crosspoints, called a *crossbar switch* or *matrix switch*. For brevity, any switching matrix of this type is called a *matrix*.

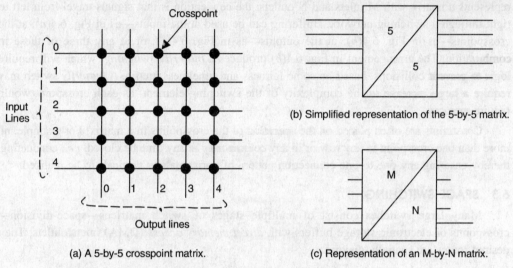

(a) A 5-by-5 crosspoint matrix.

(b) Simplified representation of the 5-by-5 matrix.

(c) Representation of an M-by-N matrix.

Fig. 6.3. Single-stage switching matrix

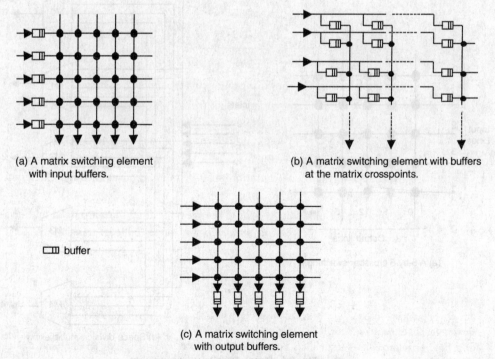

(a) A matrix switching element with input buffers.

(b) A matrix switching element with buffers at the matrix crosspoints.

▭ buffer

(c) A matrix switching element with output buffers.

Fig. 6.4. Matrix switching elements with buffers

Each elementary switching element, or crosspoint, is functionally a single-pole or multi-pole, single-throw switch, or an electrical connection, which may be made or broken by some means of control. Crosspoints may be made of metallic contacts, *e.g.*, reed relays or crossbar switches, or semiconductor gates. Figure 6.3(*a*) represents a switching matrix that connects a set of five horizontal conductors to a set of five vertical conductors by means of 25 crosspoints. The black circles in the diagram each represent a crosspoint. In order to simplify block diagrams of switches, the representation in Fig. 6.3(*b*) is substituted for that in Fig. 6.3(*a*). More generally, Fig. 6.3(*c*) represents a matrix with M inlets and N outlets; the convention is that signals travel from left to right through a switching network. Buffering can be used at the inputs—as in Fig. 6.4(*a*); at the crosspoints—as in Fig. 6.4(*b*); at the outputs—as in Fig. 6.4(*c*); or at any three of these in combination. The arrangement in Fig. 6.4(*b*) produces a *butterfly switching*, which will require logic to prevent collisions, based on some fairness and timeliness metric. A *butterfly* switch may require a large increase in the complexity of the switching element, as each crosspoint would require memory.

Constraints are often placed on the operation of the crosspoints in a matrix. For example, no more than one crosspoint in any row or in any column may at any time be closed, *i.e.*, conducting, thereby ensuring any one-to-one connection pattern of horizontals to verticals to be realized.

6.3 SPACE SWITCHING

Many large switches consist of multiple stages of switch matrices—space-division—crosspoints or electronic storage buffers with *direct memory access* (DMA) inlets/outlets. Their desired routes are spatially disjoint.

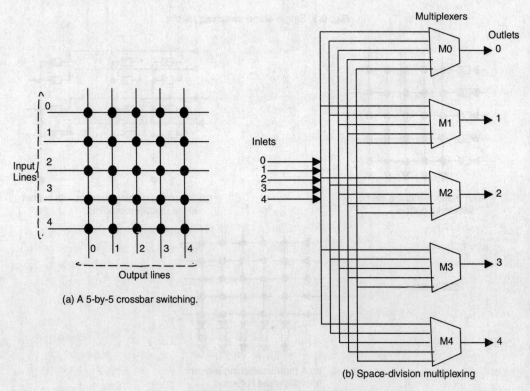

(a) A 5-by-5 crossbar switching.

(b) Space-division multiplexing

Fig. 6.5. Space-Division switching

With the constraints placed on the operation of the crosspoints in a matrix ensuring a realized one-to-one connection pattern of horizontals to verticals, how then can one arrange or distribute parallel channels through to the outlet? The traditional way is by *multiplexing*, as shown in Fig. 6.5. The switching by this arrangement is said to be in *space-division multiplex* (SDM). Each inlet or outlet of this matrix can provide no more than one communication channel.

Most switching networks are organized into *stages* with a view to reducing the total number of crosspoints required in the matrix. Each stage consists of a column of switches. In each stage, except for the last one, each switch output is connected to a switch input on the next stage. The set of connections between adjacent stages is known as an *interconnect*. The inputs of the first stage switches form the input terminals of the switching network, and the outputs of the final stage switches form the output terminals of the switching network.

6.3.1 2-Stage Matrix

Following the convention of signals travelling from left to right through a switching network, a two-stage network for a 9-by-9 matrix is shown in Fig. 6.6. Instead of using one single 9×9 array [or switch module as in Fig. 6.6(a)], six 3×3 arrays are used comprising of three arrays for the 9 inlets (*primaries*) and another three arrays for the 9 outlets (*secondaries*). Each array in the input side will plan with one link to each array in the output side. This leads to a third reduction in the number of crosspoints from 81 to 54 (*i.e.*, $3 \times 9 + 3 \times 9$) in the corresponding single stage matrix.

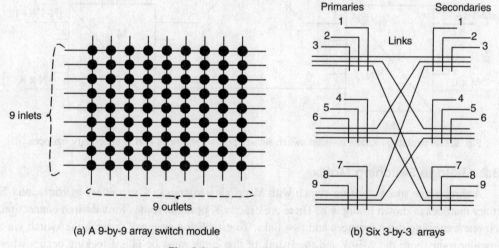

(a) A 9-by-9 array switch module   (b) Six 3-by-3 arrays

Fig. 6.6. 2-stage switching matrix

The major disadvantage of a 2-stage matrix is the possibility of internal blocking; meaning that, a particular inlet cannot connect to a free outlet due to link congestion (called *internal blocking*). For instance, when inlet 1 is connected to outlet 1, inlet 2 (or inlet 3) cannot be connected to outlet 2 or outlet 3. Attempts to establish new calls in the presence of blocking result in *traffic loss*.

A switching network is said to be *blocking* if there are one or more assignments that the switch cannot realize, so it is not always possible to set up a new call between a pair of free input and output terminals. An *assignment* is a set of calls, which are in progress, where each input or output terminal can carry at most one call. An input or output terminal is *free* if it does not carry a call. Switching networks which are not blocking are said to be *nonblocking*. Nonblocking can be subdivided into two types, namely: *strict-sense* and *rearrangeable*. In a *strict-sense nonblocking* network, there is always at least one free path, or route, through the network for a new call, where the call may be set up without rerouting existing calls. Any free route may be used without blocking ever-taking place. In a *rearrangeably nonblocking* network, new calls can always be accommodated, but it may be necessary to reroute existing calls through the network to do this.

Not all of the matrices are shown explicitly in diagrams of larger switches. Figure 6.7, for example, represents a two-stage network having N primary matrices and M secondary matrices. Notice that each connection must pass through two crosspoints and one link.

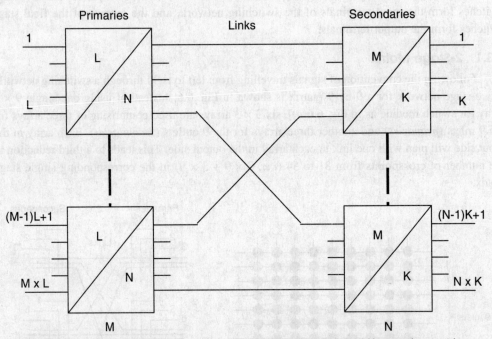

Fig. 6.7. A two-stage space division switch with M primary matrices and N secondary matrices

6.3.2 3-Stage Switching Matrix

A three-stage space-division switch with M primary matrices, K secondary matrices, and N tertiary matrices is shown in Fig. 6.8. There are exactly K possible routes for a desired connection, each one traversing three matrices and two links. To establish a new call through the switch via a particular route, both the A-link and the B-link of that route must be idle. Blocking occurs when none of the K routes has a pair of idle links.

The remarkable work of Clos (1953) demonstrated that this type of three-stage switch is *strictly* nonblocking when

$$K = L + T - 1 \tag{6.1}$$

A considerable saving in crosspoints is possible, however, when occasional blocking, is tolerated. Traffic loss becomes a concern when [Karnaugh, 1974]:

$$K < L + T - 1 \tag{6.2}$$

In addition, when

$$K \geq \max [L, T] \tag{6.3}$$

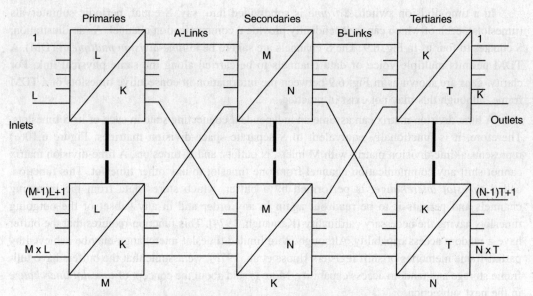

Fig. 6.8. A three-stage space-division switch with M primary matrices,
K secondary matrices and N tertiary matrices

the primary and the tertiary between which a new connection is desired will have at least one idle link on each. Blocking will then result from a failure to match idle links on any route. Condition in equation (6.3) is said to be *rearrangeably* nonblocking and is typical of a central switch for trunks and preconcentrated lines. There are variants of 3-stage switches that form switching fabrics, and still attract considerable scholarship, including Clos (1953), Beneš (1966), Banyan (butterfly) [Spanke, 1987; Haney and Christensen, 1997], and Fat Trees [Kim et al., 1996]. A switching fabric is made from many smaller switching elements and/or from buffered switching elements not necessarily of space switches. A particular switching fabric is characterised by the types and interconnection of its switching elements. This characterisation becomes evident in Section 6.5.

6.4 TIME SWITCHING

In the previous space-switching example, there is no choice of output port because every bit or call entering via an inlet port exits via the *one* outlet port. Time switching matrix can only permute the time order of the inlet samples because the samples are of equal length, which are transmitted from each channel in turn. The space occupied by each channel is called a *timeslot*. After a sample has been transmitted from each channel, the sequence of timeslots starts again, consisting of the next sample from each channel (Fig 6.9). This sequence is called a *frame* (also called the *fundamental time period*) with the voice channel that a sample belongs to being denoted by its position within this frame.

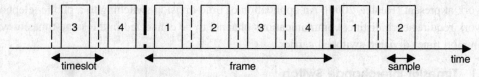

Fig. 6.9. A time-division multiplexed frame; each sample 1, 2, 3, 4 with consecutive timeslot

In a time-division switch, a *frame* is subdivided into, say, S equal, periodic subintervals (timeslots), each of which can independently provide a communication channel. As an illustration, S equates to four as in Fig. 6.9. The S channels are said to be in *time-division multiplex* (TDM). A TDM permits multiple voice or data channels to be carried along the same physical link. For clarity, gaps are shown as in Fig. 6.9 between the information in consecutive timeslots of a TDM frame, although this may not exist in practice.

A time-division matrix can assume an independent connecting state in each of its S timeslots. Therefore, it is functionally equivalent to S separate space-division matrices. Figure 6.10(*a*) represents a time-division matrix with M inlets, N outlets, and K timeslots. A time-division matrix cannot shift any communication channel from one timeslot to any other timeslot. This function, called *timeslot interchange*, is performed by a buffer, which stores data from the incoming channels and permits it to be read out again in any order and in any subset of the outgoing timeslots having the necessary cardinality [Karnaugh, 1974]. This function requires that the buffer have a random access capability. Although more limited timeslot interchange may be achieved by partial-frame memories or shift registers [Inose et al., 1973], we assume that the buffers have full-frame storage and random access capability. More is said about the concept of *timeslot interchange* in the next subsection.

Figure 6.10(*b*) shows the representation for a buffer having P input timeslots and R output timeslots. This buffer can provide no more than the minimum of P and R channels of communication. It is the time-switching analogue of a matrix with P inlets and R outlets.

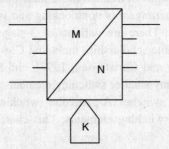

(a) Representation of a time division matrix with M inlets, N outlets, and K timeslots.

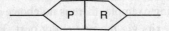

(b) Representation of a buffer with P input timeslots, and R output timeslots.

Fig. 6.10. The time-division matrix and the buffer

In conclusion, a key element in building a time-division-multiplexed (TDM) switch is the timeslot interchange. TDM permits multiple voice or data channels to be carried along the same physical link. Until recently, TDM was the principle under which almost the entire telephone network operated, and an understanding of it is hence fundamental to appreciating the state of the network at present [Hunter, 2000]. An application of time-division switching to a public telephone network requires each distinct communications channel to be connected in the same timeslot with a common time- division-switched carrier.

6.4.1 Timeslot interchange Switch

For completeness, a *timeslot interchange* (TSI) switch accepts a stream of TDM signal on its input, then rearranges the order of the timeslots within each frame and outputs the new frames. Of course, this interchange will be under the control of a control unit. As an illustration, Fig. 6.11(a) shows frames of four timeslots undergoing timeslot interchange by having their timeslots put in a different order.

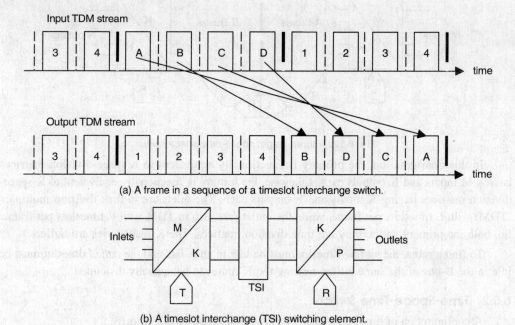

(a) A frame in a sequence of a timeslot interchange switch.

(b) A timeslot interchange (TSI) switching element.

Fig. 6.11. Principle of timeslot interchange switching

In general, *timeslot interchangers* work by writing each frame into a buffer memory and then reading the information out in a different order onto the output. In practice, the line or channel is logically partitioned, time wise, into regular timeslots. As an illustration, consider two subscribers on each side of the TSI switch as in Fig. 6.11(b). The two subscribers will each be allocated a timeslot. When the two subscribers want to communicate, as one subscriber's slot passes through the TSI switch, its timeslot is interchanged with that of the user on the other side. The constraint though is the size of this kind of switching element, which is limited by the memory access speed of the hardware.

6.5   SWITCHING FABRICS

From the two (space and time) switching arrangements discussed in the previous sections, many useful switching fabrics can be realized. The switching fabrics are usually written as a listing of the order in which the stages are connected, with an S representing space switch and a T representing a time switch. Typical combinations are TS, ST, TST, STS, TSST, and TSSST. Common switching fabrics are time-space-time (TST) and space-time-space (STS): the most popular being the TST. Both the STS and TST configurations are briefly explained in the next two subsections.

6.5.1   Space-Time-Space Switch

A schematic diagram of a space-time-space (STS) switch is shown in Fig. 6.12.

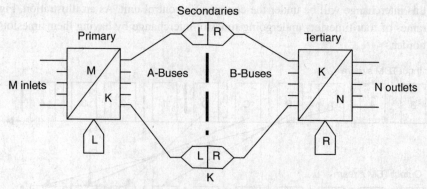

Fig. 6.12. A three-stage, space-time-space switch

In this configuration, the primary is functionally equivalent to L space-division matrices having M inputs and K outputs each. Likewise, the tertiary is functionally equivalent to R space-division matrices having K inputs and N outputs each. The inlets are in time division multiplex (TDM) with L timeslots per frame, while the outlets are also in TDM with R timeslots per frame. So, both the primary and tertiary are time-division matrices. The K secondaries are buffers.

To find a route, the *calling* timeslot must be idle in an A-bus and the *called* timeslot must be idle in the B-bus of the same buffer, making the K routes to be spatially disjointed.

6.5.2 Time-Space-Time Switch

A configuration of time-space-time (TST) switch is shown in Fig. 6.13.

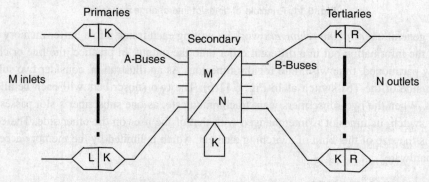

Fig. 6.13. A three-stage, time-space-time (TST) switch

The inlet and outlet channels are time-division multiplexed on each of the M inlet-lines and N of the outlet-lines. There are L timeslots per frame at the inlets and R timeslots per frame at the outlets. All the frames have equal periodic timeslots. The secondary is a time-division matrix having K timeslots. In this TST switch, both the primaries and tertiaries are buffers. Unlike the STS, the K routes are not spatially disjoint because each route occupies a different timeslot in the same physical pair of buses. Each **bus** provides K links for any desired connection in time-division multiplex. Like the STS, blocking occurs when there is no matching idle pair of links; but the TST matching must occur in time. The secondary matrix cannot permute timeslots.

6.6 SWITCH DESIGN AND SWITCHING SECURITY

Designing a switch is a complex issue, which must be approached from the perspective of systems operational requirements. The requirements will guide towards the essential systems to evolve. For instance, certain requirements ensuring that a switch matrix is properly designed include

    o Transparency between switching terminals, and the capability to switch between the network's terminals as well as subscribers interfacing with them.

    o Establishing the control and monitoring procedure of the connections in the switching array.

    o Allowance for modular growth in capacity and functionality.

    o Maintenance of high system availability and survivability even in the face of system failure.

Design and implementation strategies must evolve at improving trunk-switching security ensuring

    o greater diversity of both switching and transmission plant,

    o greater reserve capacity for both switching and transmission plant, and

    o improved network control.

With the continuation of the information revolution, telecommunications will continue to be crucial to our society of which switching remains an integral part. The robustness and reliability of switching systems is vital to the society ability to depend on telecommunications.

6.7 SUMMARY

This chapter has provided some insights into the fundamental principles of switching operation. New technology in optical switching, though based on the afore-discussed switching fabrics, is gaining momentum. Optical switching allows for *wavelength division multiplexing* (WDM) that may involve a multitude of signals multiplexed onto one fibre, each signal being at a different optical wavelength. The imprint of this is that optical switching will allow fibre ducts (typically containing 96 fibres with provision for future larger capacity by virtue of nanotechnology) to transport more traffic even once they are fully utilized by single-wavelength systems. WDM switching will consist of *optical crossconnects*—to be used in the top layer of the network. Optical crossconnects will be a crucial part of future optical WDM mesh networks, forming the basis of the network nodes and allowing long-term connections to be provisioned.

In any switching arrangements, call rearrangement requires connections to be dynamically rerouted in the network; meaning that, old connections are reestablished over new paths to make room for new connections in a process known as call rearrangement. Generally, in any switching type and application, call rearrangement must not disturb end-to-end continuity of the connection.

QUESTIONS

1. By placing buffers at the outputs of element, would the network produce a non-blocking switching? Explain.

2. A large number of identical switching elements are connected together in a network. What sort of interconnection would you suggest? What useful properties would you outline to make the network feasible? Will the network susceptible to blocking?

3. Design a fast, multilayered switching device that utilizes the basic switching principles. Write an algorithm that routes calls in the switching device.

4. Why is timeslot interchange (TSI) necessary in front of a crossbar in a time-space-time circuit switching?

5. Design a time-space-time switch with TSIs at the input lines and output lines. Include the input samples and the crossbar schedules in your design, and trace the output samples.

7

COMMUNICATIONS SATELLITE

This chapter gives an overview of satellites and their applications with regard to public telecommunications network. Small satellites (called miniaturized satellites) of different designation is becoming systems of choice due to their rapid deployment in lower altitude, short revisit times, and low cost. Importantly, these satellites have sufficient resolution in discerning areas of interest, and have found their applications most useful in the areas of communications, search and rescue, surveillance or other related operational matters. This class of satellites is also discussed in this chapter.

7.1 SATELLITES: AN OVERVIEW

A satellite is an object that orbits around something else—for example, around a planet—in an elliptical or circular path. The moon orbits around the earth, and it is a natural satellite. However, there are artificial (manmade) satellites, which are usually closer to Earth than the natural satellites. The designation of satellites is dictated by the functions performed, which are classified as follows:

o Research comprising atmospheric science, marine science, and earth science—keeping track of the Earth environment;

o Navigational including positioning—(e.g., global positioning systems, GPS—more is said of GPS in chapter 8, section 8.2.2.1.2);

o Earth observing—surface mapping and estimation;

Fig. 7.1. A communications satellite orbiting the Earth. (Image: Courtesy NASA)

  o Communications-transmitting and receiving voice, data and video information;

  o Meteorological—weather forecasting and observations; and

  o Military satellites—including communication, guidance, surveillance—eyes in the sky.

Figure 7.1 shows a communications satellite in an orbital position in space. Many types of orbits exist, but most artificial satellites orbiting Earth travel in one of four types: (1) earth-synchronous (*e.g.*, geosynchronous and geostationary), high altitude, (2) medium altitude, (3) sun-synchronous, polar, and (4) low altitude.

Satellite orbits have a variety of shapes. Some are circular, while others are highly elliptical (egg-shaped). Orbits also vary in altitude. Some circular orbits, for example, are just above the atmosphere at an altitude of about 250 kilometers, while others are more than 32,200 kilometers above Earth. The greater the altitude, the longer the orbital period, *i.e.*, the time it takes a satellite to complete one orbit. Most orbits of these four types are circular.

In this chapter, we are interested in communications satellites.

7.2 COMMUNICATIONS SATELLITES

A communications satellite orbits around the Earth to receive and retransmit radio signals, which are amplified, sorted and routed. New generation communications satellites have onboard microprocessors that facilitate switching, routing and rerouting of the radio signals. In addition, these satellites are likely to have many uplink beams and many downlink beams, and steerable, where each of the beams could cover a rather small spot (several hundred kilometres across) on the earth. Steerability implies that the beams can be moved quickly to a different spot on the earth in a matter of milliseconds, so that one beam can provide uplink or downlink services to a number of locations. Moving the beams in a regular scheduled manner would allow the satellite to gather uplink traffic from a number of locations, store it on board, and then transmit it back to earth when a downlink beam comes to rest on the intended destination.

The size and the orbit in which the satellites are positioned assist in their classification; for example, communications satellites typically use *geostationary* (or *geosynchronous*) orbits, *Molniya* (translates to lightning in Russian), or *low earth* orbits.

A *geostationary* orbit is directly above the Earth's equator: zero-degree latitude, and zero orbital eccentricity [see Fig 7.2(*a*)]. Satellites placed into this orbit are called geostationary satellites. The plane of orbit for the geosynchronous satellites is generally not the equatorial plane but their period of rotation exactly matches the Earth's rotation. Typically, geosynchronous and geostationary satellites orbit at 35,788 km above the surface of the planet (42,000 km from its centre). It takes about 24 hours to complete a rotation, and the geostationary satellites path follows the equatorial plane of the Earth. As a result, geostationary satellites do not move North or South during the day and are permanently fixed above one point on the equator. Due to the constant zero-degree latitude, satellite locations may differ by longitude only. The majority of communications satellites in service are geostationary satellites.

The one disadvantage (for some purposes) of the geosynchronous orbit is that the time to transmit a signal from earth to the satellite and back is approximately 250 milliseconds: this time delay could be annoying for telephone conversations, but insignificant for data transmission and most other uses.

A *Molniya* orbit is a highly elliptical orbit, which enables it to appear to hover above one point on the Earth for most of the day as a result of apogee dwell, with an inclination of 63.4

(a) Geostationary Orbiting Satellite

Fig. 7.2. Earth-synchronous and Sun-synchronous satellite. [Images: Courtesy NASA]

degrees and an orbital period of about 12 hours. Satellites placed in Molniya orbit are used for communications at high latitudes, examples being in Russia and Canada. In 24 hours, a Molniya-orbit satellite can move over the Earth in a figure-of-eight pattern centred on a fixed longitude; it can move slowly where it is useful, and quickly where it is of little use.

Low Earth Orbit (LEO) is an orbit within an altitude of 160 km and 2,000 km above the Earth. Satellites placed in low Earth orbits travel round the earth very quickly; one complete orbit normally takes 90 minutes. LEO satellites have very short lifetimes (in the order of months) compared with geostationary satellites (in the order of decades). There are subsets of LEO. The reader who desires a deeper knowledge of basic classification of earth orbiting satellites is referred to the author's *Satellite Communication Engineering* (Marcel Dekker, 2002).

A brief discussion on sun-synchronous (or helio-synchronous) orbit satellites is given, for completeness. A sun-synchronous, polar orbit has a fairly low altitude and passes almost directly over the North and South poles, as seen in Fig. 7.2(*b*). A slow drift of the orbit's position is coordinated with Earth's movement around the Sun in such a way that the satellite always crosses the equator at the same local time on Earth. Because the satellite flies over all latitudes, its instruments can gather information on almost the entire surface of Earth. Most meteorological satellites orbit the Earth about 15 to 16 times a day, making close, detailed observations of weather (*e.g.*, cloud cover, temperature, air pressure, precipitation, and the chemical composition of the atmosphere) over the entire Earth. It should be noted that some weather satellites are placed in high altitude, geosynchronous orbits. From these orbits, they can always observe weather activity over nearly half the surface of Earth at the same time. These satellites photograph changing cloud formations. They also produce infrared images, which show the amount of heat coming from Earth and the clouds.

Modern satellites have a wet-mass (including fuel) of several tons, compared with just 180 kilograms for Sputnik—the first manmade satellite—developed and launched in 1958 by the Soviet[1]. Modern satellites are placed in space using launch vehicles. The combined development and deployment cost of a satellite prices it out of the reach of most of the developing economies. To arrest this technology gap, an increasing number of the developing economies appear to be shifting towards miniaturized satellites. This shift serves three purposes: marking their presence in space; affordable cost, *i.e.*, less costly to manufacture and deploy and can be piggybacked on rockets with the launch of larger satellites; as well as meeting some of the perennial communications and technological needs. Most miniaturized satellites are placed in the low-earth orbit, some placed in elongated (elliptical) orbits (that swing and change from high altitude to low distance—from 40,000 to 200 km high. Developed economies are also deploying miniaturized satellites for different purposes: to support existing market, filling the gaps, or for high definition imagery.

Miniaturized satellites are designated by their maximum weight, as shown in Table 7.1.

Table 7.1. Wet mass (including fuel) of miniaturized satellites

Types of satellite	Wet mass (kg)
Minisatellite	100–500
Microsatellite	10–100
Nanosatellite	1–10
Picosatellite	0.1–1

Whether miniaturized or massive, all satellites have the same basic subsystems and use the same technologies. Many satellites require minor adjustments of their orbit before they begin to perform their function; built-in rockets—called thrusters—make these adjustments. Once a satellite is placed into a stable orbit, it can remain there for a long time without further adjustments.

7.2.1 Components of A Communications Satellite

Every communications satellite has three basic components: satellite, source, and destination ground stations, illustrated in Fig. 7.3. The exact nature of the three components will differ; it depends on the orbit and the system architecture. Each component is comprised of several subsystems. Subsystems are groups of devices that help the instruments work together and keep the satellite operating. With the arrangement in Fig. 7.3, satellite wireless communications requires only one hop, from the base station to the satellite and back down to the signal destination.

Every communications satellite in its simplest form (whether low earth or geosynchronous) involves the transmission of radio signals (information) from an originating ground station to the satellite (the uplink), followed by a retransmission of the information from the satellite back to the

---

[1]Until dissolved in 1991, a union of sixteen Socialist Republics grew to become the Union of Soviet Republics (USSR). The dominant republic now constitutes Russia.

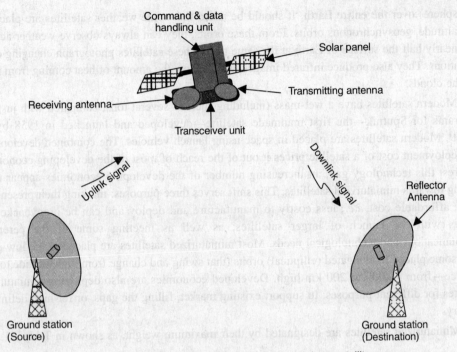

Fig. 7.3. Major components of a communications satellite

ground (the downlink). The downlink may be to a select number of (destination) ground stations, or it may be *broadcast* to everyone in a large area containing a number of ground stations. During each contact, the satellite transmits information and receives instructions. For this transaction to occur, the satellite must have a receiver and a transmitter (or a combined transmitter and receiver called *transceiver*), a receive antenna, and a transmit antenna, some method for connecting the uplink to the downlink for retransmission (command and data handling subsystem), and a prime electrical power subsystem to run all of the electronics.

A communications satellite needs large antenna reflectors to send telephone, data, or video signals. One of the biggest differences between a low earth satellite and a geosynchronous satellite is in their antennas. A geosynchronous antenna reflector can be as long as 25 metres and higher gain (typically four times) than the LEO. This is one of the primary ways that the geosynchronous satellite makes up for the apparently larger transmitter power, which it requires.

All working satellites need power to operate. The Sun provides power to most of the satellites orbiting Earth. The power subsystem generates, stores, and distributes the satellite's electric power. The power subsystem may include panels of solar cells that gather energy from the sun and backup units when the solar cells are inaccessible to Sun; that is, during night time, eclipse and/or when the photovoltaic storage is low. The solar arrays on each satellite may span more than 20 metres from tip to tip, depending on type and orbital placement.

The command and data handling subsystem consists of microprocessors (computers) that gather and process data from the instruments and execute commands from Earth, as well as pointing control system. Pointing control system keeps the satellite steady and pointing in the right direction. The system uses sensors, like eyes, so the satellite can "see" where it is pointing. The type of pointing control a satellite needs depends on its mission. A satellite making scientific observations needs a more precise steering system than a communications satellite does.

The ground station system provides the link between the satellite in orbit and on the ground 'operations control and processing centre'. A ground station system consists of several subsystems namely: an antenna pedestal and a reflector (typically surface parabolic dish), antenna feed, noise amplifier and down converter, and feed controller and environmental monitoring facility. The down-converted signals are fed into the base controller, data storage and data transmission facility, and local display workstation. The antenna feed-controller facilitates accuracy pointing ensuring contact with the satellite during satellite passes. An auto-tracking and program-tracking unit resides with other instrumentation at the ground stations.

7.2.2 System Design Process

The processes involved in the design of a satellite and related system components are beyond the scope of this book. However, readers requiring deeper understanding of the satellites' components relating to their theory—including figure of merit, link calculation, security and error detection and correction coding schemes, etc, and their design process, and implementation-are referred to the excellent book by this author (*Satellite Communication Engineering*, published by Marcel Dekker, 2002).

7.2.3 Choice of Operational frequencies

The choice of operational frequencies is the fundamental difference between the satellites. These frequencies extend from P band (0.2–1.0 GHz) to Ka band (26.5–40.0 GHz). The geostationary satellites have different uplink and downlink frequencies: mostly in the C and K bands. Typical frequencies are shown in Table 7.2.

Table 7.2. Typical satellite operating frequencies

Band	Uplink frequency (GHz)	Downlink frequency (GHz)
C	5.9–7.1	3.7–4.2
Ku	14.0–14.5	11.7–12.2
Ka	27.5–31.0	17.7–21.2

Each national telecommunications regulatory body in compliance with the International Telecommunication Union (ITU) Recommendations, which the national regulatory body subscribes to, allocates these frequencies. Satellites that provide reliable station-to-station transmission of signals of all kinds including television, telephone and Internet services operate in the C Band, or lower frequency.

7.2.4 Systems Protection in Space

Space is a very aggressive environment. Satellite onboard electronics need to be rigorously tested and modified to be "space hardened" or resistant to the outer space environment (vacuum, microgravity, thermal extremes, and radiation exposure). Thus, the satellite is thermally insulated against the harsh space environment. This insulation must be capable of resisting up to 2800°C and all onboard electronics be able to survive a total radiation dose rate of 100 K rads per annum.

7.3 SERVICE OBLIGATION OF SATELLITES

Satellite services are used to satisfy service obligation in the provision of telecommunication services to inaccessible terrain, and very remote areas, where terrestrial options are not available.

Satellite transmission can also be used to provide short-term services in advance of terrestrial infrastructure.

Satellite technology is suitable for specialist applications, particularly where common information is to be shared between a number of sites. This technology has been used for special events where voice, data, audio program lines, etc, need to be provided for a short-term basis. Special events include sporting, inauguration, and emergency situations like the April 2005 Pope Benedict XVI's inauguration; April and August 2006 hurricane Katrina devastation of New Orleans and Asian Tsunami respectively; 2007 devastating storm across southern floodplain of Bangladesh; 2008 China seismic disaster and Beijing Olympic games.

7.4 SUMMARY

Communications satellite is a spacecraft in orbit around the Earth that receives and transmits or retransmits radio signals. Modern communications satellites have onboard processors that enable signal amplification and sorting or routing these signals. An overview of the basic functionalities of satellites has been presented in this chapter. Also discussed are new generation, small (miniaturized) satellites, which are becoming systems of choice due to their rapid deployment in lower altitude, short revisit times, low cost and sufficient resolution in discerning areas of interest in terms of search and rescue, surveillance or operational matters.

QUESTIONS

1. A large number of countries have joined the space communications race, and have placed or intending to place their geosynchronous satellites in orbit. There are a limited number of "slots" for satellites. An international governing body (ITU) regulates the allocation of these slots. Discuss how these slots can be distributed equitably.

2. New generation satellites are likely to have, in addition to onboard microprocessors, many uplink beams and many downlink beams, which would be steerable where each of beams covers a rather small spot on the earth. As a designer, write a program that will perform this function, and demonstrate this functionality by simulation.

3. What issues will you consider if tasked to design a communications network capable of providing round-the-clock coverage of your country? Discuss the approach you will undertake.

8

MOBILE COMMUNICATIONS NETWORK

The deployment and the increasing use of satellite systems have aided wireless and mobile communications. Mobile communication is another means of providing service. Cellular telephony is a product of wireless technology. This technology has enabled mobility; for instance, the ability to communicate with anyone, anywhere, and at anytime. To facilitate mobility paradigm, the system-user interface should be as simple as that of ordinary landline telephone offered by the public telephone network. Also, to keep up and running a mobile communications network, the network designer must consider three issues, namely; the assignment of the cell base stations, the choice of the antennas (*e.g.*, whether omni- or sectored- directionality), and the assignment of the appropriate carrier frequencies to each cell or sector.

This chapter explains the principle of mobile communications network including the engineering of the systems that enable mobile communication and that facilitate mobility; for instance, base stations and mobile switching station, as well as location of mobile systems.

8.1 OVERVIEW

Mobile communications (or wireless) network is a means of providing telecommunication services. Such a network allows mobility; that is, requiring on demand, anywhere, anytime operations. The term *mobility* is a very generic term that refers to personal, terminal or service moveability. For instance, *service mobility* refers to the capacity of a system to hide server-interface specifics from the users via a generic acquisition mechanism. Whereas *personal mobility* refers to mobile-users migration from one network to another without being tied down to a particular location and/or to a specific timeframe. Advances in wireless technology have allowed users to an unprecedented access to telecommunication services via their 'mobile devices' such as palm-size and personal computers, cellular telephones, handheld devices, car directional finder using GPS, etc. As a result, mobility is becoming increasingly important for business, whether one is expanding a business or managing a work, and life balance while on the move.

8.2 MOBILE COMMUNICATIONS NETWORK ARCHITECTURE

A mobile communications network is composed of several functional entities whose functions and interfaces are specified. Figure 8 can represent a generic mobile communications network where the network is divided into three broad subsystems namely: Mobile Station, the Base Station and the Mobile services Switching Centre. A *mobile station* (MS) is the mobile unit or device operated by the subscriber, which operates on an air interface (denoted by U_m in the literature). Simply, an MS is your telephone handset.

In the mobile communications network arrangement, any mobile stations using the services of the *public telephone network* (*e.g.*, PSTN) can communicate both signalling and bearer traffic to the *base station subsystem* (BSS) particularly via its *base transceiver station* (BTS), which provides the most favourable *radio frequency*, RF, signal. BSS ensures that an association is always established between the MS's geographic location and the closest BTS. When an MS moves from the coverage area of a BTS to another, the first association is released and a new one is formed. This procedure is called *handover* or *handoff*. More is said about the process of switching over offered traffic from one radio cell to another in Section 8.2.3.3.

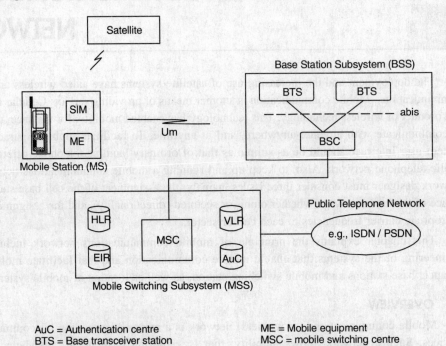

AuC = Authentication centre   ME = Mobile equipment
BTS = Base transceiver station   MSC = mobile switching centre
BSC = Base station controller   SIM = Subscriber Identity Module
EIR = Equipment identification register   VLR = Visitor location register
HLR = Home location register   abis, Um = interfaces

Fig. 8.1. Architecture of a mobile communications network

MSS is the network subsystem: the main part of which is the *mobile switching centre* (MSC), which performs the switching of calls between the mobile users, and between mobile and fixed network users. The *base station controller* (BSC)—a component of BSS- and MSC manage radio resource, channel assignments, and handle mobility management operations and handover services. A single BSC may control multiple BTSs. A single MSC may control multiple BSCs. The communication link between BSS and MSS is across the A interface. The next subsections give an overview of the elements that constitute each subsystem.

8.2.1 MOBILE STATION

The mobile station (MS) consists of the mobile equipment (the terminal) and a smart card (called the *Subscriber Identity Module*, SIM). The SIM provides personal mobility, allowing the user to have access to subscribed services irrespective of a specific terminal. For example, by inserting a SIM card into another GSM or AMPS terminal, the user is able to receive at, and make calls from that terminal, and receive other subscribed services. AMPS (Advanced Mobile Phone System) is a first-generation cellular technology that uses separate frequencies, or channels, (*e.g.*, 800/900 MHz frequency range) for each conversation. AMPS is expected to be phased out in

February 2008 and be replaced by CDMA2000 series or GSM, which operates on digital standard capable of supporting multiple voice calls and data services on the same channel. GSM is a second-generation (2G) digital system based on terrestrial switched network, whose functional-architecture is based on the *open systems interconnection* (OSI) model, designed to permit functional partitioning. GSM borrowed heavily from ISDN and SS$_7$ protocols and physical connections. GSM has evolved further; now 3G+ with more features.

Two registers, the *International Mobile Equipment Identity* (IMEI)—uniquely identifies each subscribers mobile equipment, and *International Mobile Subscriber Identity* (IMSI)—identifies the subscriber to the network, facilitate personal mobility as well as the identity of the subscriber to be traced. Each SIM card contains an IMSI, a secret key for authentication, and other information.

With the advent of Very Large Scale Integration (VLSI) microprocessor technology, many functions of the mobile station have been built on one chipset, resulting in lighter, more compact, and more energy-efficient terminals. Advances in the nanotechnology area will further see more compactness in chipsets manufacturing resulting in the inclusion of a myriad of features and functionalities into one chipset. More is said about nanotechnology in chapter 10.

8.2.2 Base Station System Engineering

A *base station subsystem* (BSS) provides the interface between a *mobile switching subsystem* (MSS) and a mobile station (MS). The architecture of BSS in a cellular telephony network is shown in Fig 8.2. A BSS is functionally divided into two subsystems, namely; base transceiver subsystem (BTS), and base station controller (BSC), each of which has several component parts. Each subsystem is discussed under appropriate heading.

The BSS contains the physical equipment essential to providing radio coverage in at least one cell but typically in multiple cells.

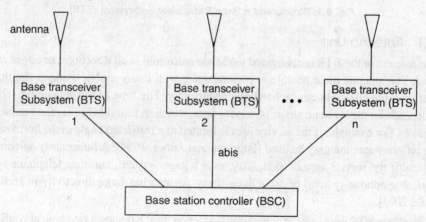

Fig. 8.2. Structure of a Base Station Subsystem (BSS)

The interface between BTS and BSC is called *abis*. Trunked and cellular systems transmit several control and traffic channels that must be coupled to the same antenna system [Hernando and Perez-Fontan, 1999]. As a result, the BSS must contain the necessary hardware and software to communicate directly with MS and must also be capable of handling cross-carrier channel sharing; that is, handling traffic across multiple sectors or carriers. To achieve this, specific RF devices, such as transmitter combiners, duplexers or multiplexers, and receiver couplers, are used.

The BTS and BSC may co-locate, or the BSC may locate at the MSS. The location arrangement of BTS and BSC determines the traffic model to be used in investigating the network's traffic handling performance. More is said about the traffic handling performance analysis in chapter 9.

8.2.2.1 *Base Transceiver Subsystem*

The primary function of a base transceiver subsystem (BTS) is to provide RF radiation and reception with suitable channel access mechanism and traffic communications interface between MSC and itself. A schematic diagram of a BTS is shown in Fig. 8.3, which comprises of an antenna unit, signal-processing unit, call controller unit, and traffic interface unit. The functions of each of the blocks comprising BTS are briefly described in the next paragraphs.

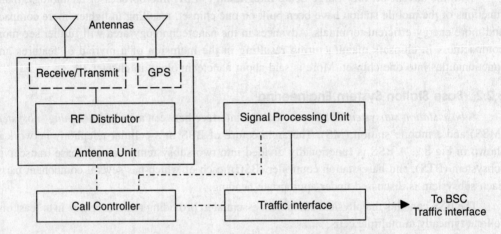

Fig. 8.3. Structure of a Base Transceiver Subsystem (BTS)

8.2.2.1.1 Antenna Unit

The antenna of the BTS is configured to radiate uniformly in all directions, or aimed at specific directions. The antenna must be able to communicate with many mobile stations simultaneously such that multiple channels can be handled concurrently. The type of antenna employed by base station depends on the size and shape of service area, which in turn determines the number of cells and channels. For example, if the service area is limited to a restricted angle in the horizontal plane, a corner reflector antenna may be used [Fujimoto and James, 1994]. A linear array antenna may be used instead if the service area is wide, (*e.g.*, as in a pager system, maritime telephone system, or aeronautical telephone system) because linear array antenna has large directivity in vertical plane [Kolawole, 2003].

Typically, a BTS uses one omnidirectional antenna. Fig. 8.4 shows two typical configurations of a multi-channel, antenna system. The type in Fig. 8.4(*a*) uses two antennas, one for the transmitters and the other for the receivers. The type in Fig. 8.4(*b*) uses a single antenna rack for both transmitters and receivers, whereby it is coupled to the transceiver by means of a duplexer. Either of the antenna arrangements in Fig. 8.4(*a*) or Fig. 8.4(*b*) is capable of producing and receiving RF radiation, but system gain requirement, space restriction, and/or economic factors determine any choice.

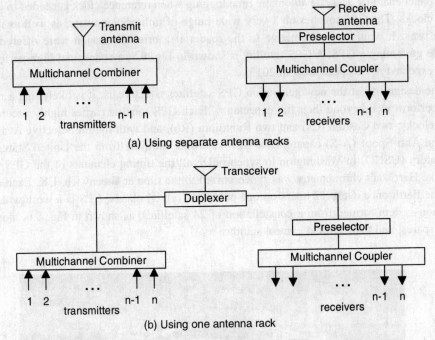

(a) Using separate antenna racks

(b) Using one antenna rack

Fig. 8.4. Types of antenna connection of a multichannel system

8.2.2.1.2 GPS

Precise time dissemination is critical to the synchronization of telecommunications networks. Within both wired and wireless systems, consistent pulses and time intervals are used to manage information flow through the network nodes. In particular, the *public telephone network* (*e.g.*, PSTN or ISDN) relies on accurate timing information for the proper digital transmission of voice and data [Brutt, 1999]. A *global positioning system* (GPS) connection is provided to the receiver's

Fig. 8.5. A new generation, high performance, GPS satellite. [Image: courtesy NASA]

control panel enabling accurate automatic time logging when reference clock is needed to generate system clocks. The GPS touches on a very wide range of military hardware, as well as its many civilian uses. It would be informative to the reader if a brief discussion were offered on the principle governing a GPS. A GPS satellite is shown in Fig. 8.5; a conceptual high-performance system expected to be operational in 2013.

The design life of the new generation GPS satellites is 7.3 years: it is likely that a majority would perform well beyond their life expectancy. Each GPS satellite carries highly accurate four atomic clocks: two Cesium (Cs) and two Rubidium (Rb), and with inbuilt Selective Availability (SA) and Anti-Spoof (A-S) capabilities. GPS satellites use time from the United States Naval Observatory (USNO) in Washington to synchronize all the timing elements of the GPS system, much like Harrison's chronometer was synchronized to the time at Greenwich, UK. Each satellite orbits the Earth once every 12 hours on one of the six orbital planes. GPS is a worldwide radio-navigation system formed from a constellation of 24 satellites, as shown in Fig. 8.6, along with several spares, and their ground control stations.

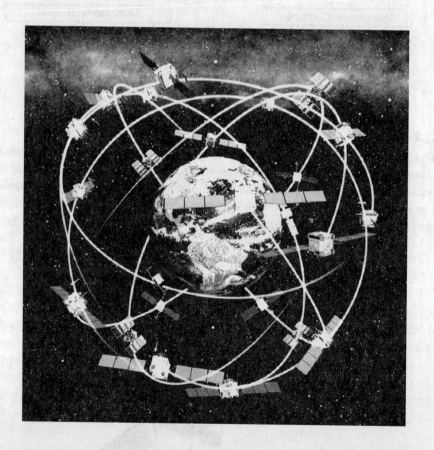

Fig. 8.6. Navstar GPS Constellation. [Image: courtesy USAF - 24 Aug., 2005]

The GPS constellation is positioned such that at any given time, 5 to 8 satellites are visible from any point on Earth. Each GPS satellite transmits a unique navigational signal centred on two L-band frequencies of the electromagnetic spectrum: *i.e.*, L_1 at 1575.42 MHz and L_2 at

1227.6 MHz, with enough power to ensure a minimum signal power level of -160 dBw at the earth's surface (the maximum is likely to reach about -153 dBw [Navstar, 1993]). Since these microwave signals are highly directional and all GPS satellites transmit on these frequencies. Each satellite has its own code. GPS receivers use *pseudorandom noise* (PRN) sequences to construct their codes. There are many types of PRN sequences, the more popular have names: Barker, M-Sequence, Gold, Walsh-Hadamard, and Kasami. A brief description of these names is given later below.

When a GPS receiver receives a signal, it compares the signals it *knows* about with what it *has* received. The way that it compares the signals is called cross-correlation. Typically, three binary codes are used that shift carrier phase frequencies, namely:

1. The *clear/access* or *coarse/acquisition* (C/A) code (sometimes referred to as the S code). The C/A codes are 1023 "chip" long binary sequences that are generated at a 1.023 MHz chip rate used primarily to acquire the P-code. The C/A code is available on the L-frequency.

2. The *precision* or *private* (P) code is a far more complex binary sequence, which is 266.4 days long approximately with a chipping rate at the fundamental frequency $f_0 = 10.23$ MHz. The P code is available on both L_1 and L_2 frequencies.

3. The Y-code is used in place of the P-code whenever the anti-spoofing (A-S) mode of operation is activated. Under A-S, the P code is encrypted through the modulation of W code, a further secret code. The sum, when encrypted is called Y code, is then modulated on the L_1 and L_2 carrier signals. The same P (or Y) code is modulated on both carrier signals, which are then propagated through the ionosphere. The ionosphere exerts some distortion, which in effect *retards* the PRN sequence, but advances the carrier phase. Of course, by line theory, a difference in signal transit time of the same PRN sequence occurs due to the retardation of the two L-band signals by a different amount as they travel through the ionosphere. The reader who desires a deeper knowledge of ray refraction through the ionosphere, including estimation of range or time delay error, refraction error and their cumulative effect on measurements is referred to the author's book: *Radar Systems, peak detection* and *tracking* (Elsevier, 2003).

Due to the spread spectrum characteristic of the signals, the system provides a large margin of resistance to interference. Each satellite transmits a navigation message containing its orbital elements, clock behavior, system time, approximate ionospheric delay model—which is a function of signal frequency, status messages and an almanac that gives the approximate data for each active satellite. This allows the GPS receiver to process the satellite distance (or range) measurements and produce its position. GPS navigation and position determination is based on measuring the distance from the user position to the precise locations of the four GPS satellites as they orbit. Due to the high degree of accuracy of the GPS system, special-purpose GPS receivers are often employed as a timing source for both wireline and wireless telecommunications networks, as well as a timing reference for wide-area synchronization including electric power systems, distributed computer networks, banking (*e.g.*, for money transfers and bank time locks), manufacturing, and metrology [Brutt, 1999]. Receiver clocks do not have to be too accurate because an extra satellite range measurement can remove errors.

8.2.2.1.2.1 *PRN sequences*

A brief discussion on the more popular PRN sequences is given in this section. Attention is focused on the more popular sequences, namely: Barker sequence [Barker, 1953]; maximum length sequence (*m*-sequence) [Cohn and Lempel, 1977)]; Gold sequence [Gold, 1968)]; Walsh-Hadamard sequence [Kanjilal, 1995]; Kasami sequence [Kasami, 1966]. Note that the construction or selection of proper sequences (or sets of sequences) is not trivial. For robustness, pseudo-noise sequences we use, either for ranging or communication, must at least have length, autocorrelation, and cross-correlation properties. Specifically, the autocorrelation of a given sequence or code must have a single correlation peak with minimal sidelobes, and the cross-correlation with other members in a family can be no higher than the sidelobes of the autocorrelation. The mathematics governing these rules are not addressed, rather a general overview of what the sequences is. Readers wanting to know the background mathematics to estimating the sequences' autocorrelation and cross-correlation should consult amongst others Fan and Darnell (1996), and Sarwate and Pursley (1980). Sequences and codes are interchangeably used in the open literature.

8.2.2.1.2.1.1 Barker sequence

A Barker code is a string of digits $a_i = \pm 1$ of length $l \geq 2$ such that

$$\left| \sum_{i=1}^{l-k} a_i a_{i+k} \right| \leq 1 \qquad \text{for all} \qquad 1 \leq k < l$$

Barker codes are used for pulse compression of radar signals. There are Barker codes of lengths 2, 3, 4, 5, 7, 11, and 13. It is conjectured that no longer Barker codes exist, and that the Barker codes of lengths 2 and 4 are the only ones that are of even length. Table 8.1 lists known Barker codes up to reversal of digits and negation.

Table 8.1. A list of known Barker codes

Length of code	Code elements
2	+ −, + +
3	+ + −
4	+ − + +, + − − −
5	+ + + − +
7	+ + + − − + −
11	+ + + − − − + − − + −
13	+ + + + + − − + + − + − +

8.2.2.1.2.1.2 Maximal Length (or *m*-) sequence

M-sequences are periodic sequences generated by using shift registers, modulo-2 adders (exclusive-or, XOR, gates) with feedback-taps, as shown in Fig. 8.7. The feedback-taps (t_i) enable linear operations to be performed, where the next input is a linear function of the current state. If there are N shift-registers, then there will be up to 2^N different combinations of 0s and 1s. The length of the code equals $2^N - 1$. Thus, the number of possible codes is dependent on the number of possible sets of feedback-taps that produce an *m*-sequence.

8.2.2.1.2.1.3 Gold sequences

Gold sequences (codes) are constructed by modulo-2 adding two m-sequences of the same length with each other. By shifting one of the two m-sequences, we get a different sequence. The number of sequences that is available is $2^N + 1$ (arises when the two m-sequences alone, and a

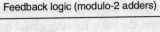

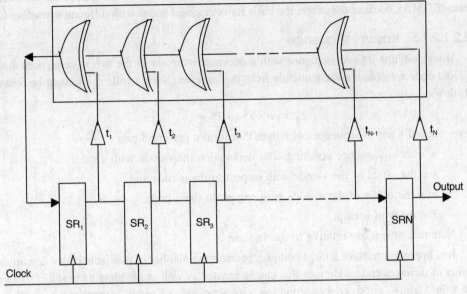

SR$_i$ = shift register
t$_i$ = feedback taps; where i = 1, 2, ..., N

Fig. 8.7. Maximum length (m-) sequence using a linear feedback logic and N-shift registers

combination with $2^N - 1$ different shift positions). The maximum full-code cross-correlation has a value of $2[(N + 2)/2] + 1$. The shifting property can be used to generate codes, which will permit multiple access on the channel.

8.2.2.1.2.1.4 Walsh-Hadamard sequence

Walsh functions are generated using an iterative process of constructing a Hadamard matrix, starting with H = [0]. The Hadamard matrix is built by

$$H_{2n} = \begin{pmatrix} H_n & H_n \\ H_n & H_n \end{pmatrix} \tag{8.1}$$

For example, consider Walsh-Hadamard sequences of length 2 and 4 respectively, thus,

$$H_2 = \begin{pmatrix} 0 & 0 \\ 0 & 1 \end{pmatrix} \qquad H_4 = \begin{pmatrix} 0 & 0 & 0 & 0 \\ 0 & 1 & 0 & 1 \\ 0 & 0 & 1 & 1 \\ 0 & 1 & 1 & 0 \end{pmatrix} \tag{8.2}$$

From the corresponding matrix, the Walsh-Hadamard codewords (w_i, i = 0, 1, 2, 3) are given by the rows. Thus,

$$\begin{align} w_0 &= [0\ 0\ 0\ 0] \\ w_1 &= [0\ 1\ 0\ 1] \\ w_2 &= [0\ 0\ 1\ 1] \\ w_3 &= [0\ 1\ 1\ 0] \end{align} \tag{8.3}$$

Usually the binary data are mapped on to polar form so that real numbers arithmetic is used when computing sequence-correlations. So, 0's are mapped to 1's and 1's are mapped to -1.

Walsh-Hadamard sequences are important in wireless systems, including *code division multiple access* (CDMA), because they form the basis for orthogonal codes with different spreading factors.

8.2.2.1.2.1.5 Kasami-sequence

If we combine a Gold-sequence with a decimated version of the two m-sequences that form the Gold-code we obtain a Kasami-code from the large set. Such a code c_k can then be formulated as follows:

$$c_k = u \cdot T^k v \cdot T^m w \qquad (8.4)$$

where u and v are *m*-sequences of length that form a preferred pair

w = an *m*-sequence resulting after decimation the *v*-code with a value.

k = the offset of the *v*-code with respect to the *u*-code and

m = the offset of the *w*-code with respect to the *u*-code.

T = delay of a chip.

Note that offsets are relative to the 1s state.

It is important to have a large code-set because the number of available codes determines the number of different code addresses that can be created as well as enabling us to select those codes that would show good cross-correlation characteristics. Kasami sequences have the same correlation properties as Gold-sequences; the difference lies in the number of codes that can be created.

8.2.2.1.3 Smart Antenna

The use of omnidirectional antennas in base station could be queried particularly as technological advances move further into multimedia-oriented applications. Many base stations are using smart (or intelligent) antenna systems. Smart antennas are broadly defined as having multibeam antennas. Smart antenna systems use multiple highly directional antennas pointing in different directions, each of which covers a sector and provides more accurate directional targeting. A simple multi-beam antenna is shown in Fig. 8.8, suitable for *very high frequency* (VHF), 50-70 MHz cellular networks.

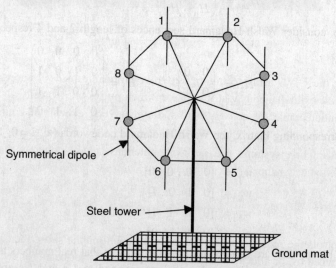

Fig. 8.8. A sketch of a multibeam, hexagonal antenna array

Another very broad bandwidth antenna arrangement that is gaining currency, in mobile communications networks, is the *Ultra-wideband* (UWB) antenna array. This type offers improved performance compared to the omnidirectional, multiband antennas. UWB antenna array can operate over a wide range of frequencies (*e.g.*, from 50 MHz to 450 MHz), and can offer multiple bands, multiple channels selection allowing several transmitters to feed one antenna. Two types of UWB antenna arrangements are shown in Fig. 8.9.

Figure 8.9(*a*) comprises of symmetrical dipoles whose aperture is formed by the length of the small elements comprising the antenna. The aperture of the scissors antenna array in Fig. 8.9(*b*) can be obtained like vertical dipole but would require additional wires (bifilar wires) connected to the ends to increase the electromagnetic qualities of the array [Gallais et al, 2003]. The bifilar wires need to match with the feed-point impedance (*i.e.*, at the reflective ground) to stabilise the bandwidth and improve directivity.

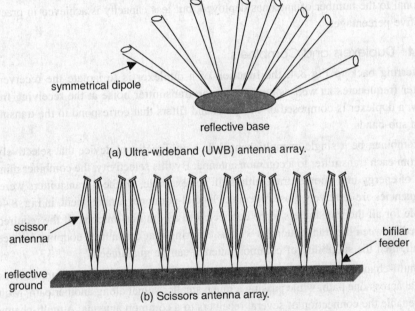

(a) Ultra-wideband (UWB) antenna array.

(b) Scissors antenna array.

Fig. 8.9. Types of ultra-wideband antenna arrays

Unlike the existing wireless technologies that transmit and receive signals on a particular radio frequency, the UWB array technology involves transmitting very short pulses on a wide range of frequencies simultaneously at low power. Such pulses are typically about 1 picoseconds (10^{-9} s) long, undetectable by conventional radio receivers, except, of course, by the UWB receivers.

The smart antenna systems use multiple antennas, phase coherent transmitters and/or receivers and sophisticated signal processing. Since radio spectrum is a limited resource shared by all subscribers, a method must be devised to divide up the bandwidth among as many users as possible. The smart antenna arrays use space separation technique (*e.g.*, *space division multiple access*, SDMA).

SDMA controls the radiated energy in space for each mobile subscriber. Each subscriber is dynamically serviced by, or allocated, a beam of energy from spot-beam (or sectored) antennas in the user's direction. The same bandwidth can be re-used in different places far enough apart (or shielded by mountains or high buildings) so that there is no significant transmission from one place to the other. The SDMA can be deployed in such a way to assign an optimal base station to a mobile system. The basis for SDMA algorithm is formed by cells and sectored antennas that constitute the infrastructure implementing space division multiplexing [Schiller, 2000]. SDMA is not used in isolation of the other access schemes, like, frequency filtering (eg, Frequency Division Multiple Access, FDMA), temporal gating (*e.g.*, *Time Division Multiple Access*, TDMA), and signature assignment (*e.g.*, *Code Division Multiple Access*, CDMA). The reader, who desires a deeper knowledge and more rigorous analysis of the frequency filtering, temporal gating, and signature assignment techniques, is referred to the author's *Satellite Communication Engineering* (Marcel Dekker, 2002). In practice, a combination of Time- and Frequency-Division Multiple Access (TDMA/FDMA) is used by the GSM.

In conclusion, smart antennas and SDMA technology provide, in addition to spectral gains, an improved coverage and range, and greater system capacity. In theory, capacity enhancement is proportional to the number of antennas deployed, but less capacity is achieved in practice: about seventy-five percentages.

8.2.2.1.4 Duplexers and Combiners

Referring back to Fig 8.4, the function of a duplexer is to isolate the receiver from the transmitter frequencies as well as attenuating the transmitter noise at the receiving frequencies. Typically, a duplexer is composed of two passband filters that correspond to the transmission and reception sub-bands.

A combiner, be it single or multichannel, is a unidirectional device that selectively transfers energy from each transmitter to a common antenna. By this selectivity, the combiner minimises the injection of energy into another transmitters. If, for example, all the n transmitters were such that their frequencies are relatively close, the multichannel-combiner arrangement, in Fig. 8.4(*a*), would be suitable for all the transmitters to be connected to a common antenna. If the required isolation is provided between the transmitters as well as ensuring that the mutual coupling between them is very small, then the suitability of common antenna can be guaranteed.

A multi-channel coupler is a directional coupler. Directional couplers are devices that will pass signal across one path, while passing a much smaller signal along another path. Multi-channel couplers enable the connection of several receivers to a common antenna. A multi-channel coupler performs three basic functions:

- Preselecting the frequencies to be received, while rejecting those that are out of the desired band (*i.e.*, passband filtering);
- Compensating for the losses of the antenna feeder and those from other interference sources (*i.e.*, using a preamplifier unit);
- Delivering the same RF power to each receiver (*i.e.*, using power splitter).

8.2.2.1.5 Signal Processing Unit

Referring back to Fig. 8.3, the *Signal Processing Unit* comprises primarily of modulators and encoders, and demodulators and decoders. The modulator generates carrier signals of, and applies suitable encoder (*e.g.*, convolutional encoder) for, voice (including supervisory audio tone, pilot and other auxiliary signals) and data.

Upon receiving the predetermined-diversity input derived from the selected receiving antennas and signal from a local oscillator, the demodulator reverses the sequence performed by the modulator. The sequence, called modulation, is whereby a signal is impressed upon a higher frequency carrier, (that is, modifying a baseband signal), in a known way to encode its content. A demodulator on the other hand performs the reverse function of a modulator, whereby the original signal is recovered from a modulated carrier and produces the desired replica of the transmitted signal. Wireless channels are time varying radio channels that are prone to multi-path fading. Part of the demodulation process is to use a decoder with error correction capability to ensure a reliable reception.

8.2.2.1.6 Call Controller

The call-controller maintains an independent setup channel for the shared use of BTS in communicating with mobiles within its coverage area. Only data traffic is transmitted on the setup channel.

8.2.2.1.7 Traffic Communications Interface

The function of the Traffic Communications Interface is to ensure that voice and data communications between the BTS and BSC over digital links operate at the required rate.

8.2.2.2 *Base Station Controller*

The base station controller (BSC) is quite intelligent, and much of the ongoing 'house keeping' activities between base transceiver subsystem (BTS) and mobile station (MS) are performed by the BSC. The BSC performs the following functions:

o Call handover (*i.e.*, locate mobiles to the radio cells with the highest signal strength),

o Call management (*i.e.*, call setup, call supervision and call termination),

o System monitoring (*i.e.*, ordered equipment testing)

o Mobile station's location (*i.e.*, identifying mobiles within a BTS and if the trace-signal invocation were to continue across activation boundary, the trace would continue a handover. In this case, the BSC will inform the new base station the trace that has been invoked when handover or handoff is performed.)

o Traffic communications interface between itself and mobile switching centre (MSC).

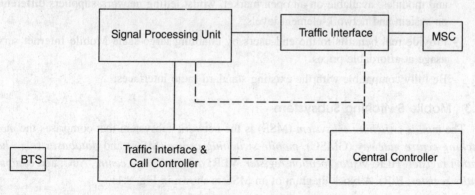

Fig. 8.10. Base Station Controller (BSC)

Figure 8.10 shows a block diagram of a BSC: it comprises a signal-processing unit, a call controller, traffic communications interface, and central controller. The interface between BSC and MSC is called the air interface. The functions of each of the blocks comprising a BSC are described briefly.

The functions performed by signal processing unit, traffic interface, and call controller are similar to their counterparts in BTS. In addition, the signal processing unit provides voice and data paths interface between the RF and MSC.

The central controller is a processor that allocates and de-allocates voice and data channels. The central controller also communicates with the BTS and MSC, and performs system monitoring. The literature has relatively sparse models that deal with traffic handling at the BS level, however the queue theory, which has considerable wide applications, is exploited to discuss traffic interaction with a network as well as providing quantitative measures of the network performance in chapter 9.

8.2.2.3 General Comments on Base Station Subsystem

The current crop of base stations uses a fraction of the radio spectrum available in order to avoid interference with adjacent cells. These base stations may have sufficiently carried the transmission capacity and application requirements of the previous and current network systems. However, with the increasing demand of systems applications by users, the current crop of base stations would require some modification to boost capacity if the demand for access is to be met. This modification has resulted in the design of a variety of evolutionary wireless networks capable of handling multimedia systems.

A new initiative was floated in 2002 that looked at a different way of designing base stations. This initiative is called the *Open Base Station Architecture Initiative* (OBSAI) [OBSAI, 2002], which intended to focus on the base station architecture and internal interfaces that would lead to modular radio base stations featuring open internal interfaces. It is envisaged that the initiative would:

- Allow faster development of innovative and more cost-effective radio base stations enabling earlier and lower-cost introduction of new technologies and services by the operators.
- Allow next-generation radio base stations to be built using best-of-breed, shared platforms and modules, available on an open market, whilst letting network suppliers differentiate on system and network-element levels.
- Provide real benefits to the end-users by enabling large-scale Mobile Internet service usage at affordable prices.
- Be fully compatible with the existing standard radio interfaces.

8.2.3 Mobile Switching Subsystem

The *mobile switching subsystem* (MSS) is the network subsystem that comprises the *mobile switching centre gateway* (GMSC), *mobile switching centre* (MSC) and *databases* (*e.g., home location register*, HLR; *visitor location register*, VLR; *authentication centre*, AuC; and *equipment identity register*, EIR). A block diagram of an MSS is shown in Fig. 8.11.

Signalling between functional entities in the MSS uses Signalling System Number 7 (SS$_7$), like in the public telephone networks. The principles of SS$_7$ have been discussed extensively in chapter 5, section 5.1.3.1.

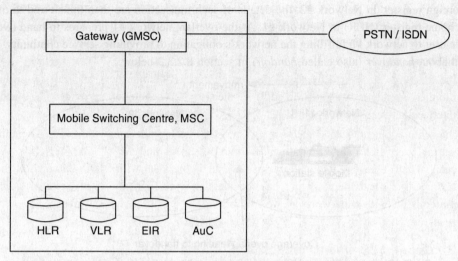

Fig. 8.11. A structure of Mobile Switching Subsystem

The *mobile switching centre gateway* (GMSC) provides the interface to the telephone networks. It is a complete telephone exchange, with capabilities for relaying calls between the fixed public switched telephone network (PSTN) and the cellular network.

8.2.3.1 *Registers*

The *home location register* (HLR) and *visitor location register* (VLR), together with the MSC, provide the call-routing and roaming capabilities of mobile networks (like GSM and CDMA2000 series). The HLR contains all the administrative information of each subscriber registered in the corresponding mobile network, along with the current location of the mobile. Typically, the location of the mobile is in the form of the signalling address of the VLR associated with the mobile station. The routing procedure may not be different to those described earlier in chapter 4. Other variants of that described in chapter 4, which are based on *graph theory* with a view to finding the shortest distance between nodes using, for example, Bellman-Ford algorithm [Bellman, 1958] and Dijkstra algorithm [Dijkstra, 1959], do exist.

The *visitor location register* (VLR) contains selected administrative information from the HLR necessary for call control and provision of the subscribed services, for each mobile currently located in the geographical area controlled by the VLR. Although each functional entity can be implemented as an independent unit, all manufacturers of switching equipment to date implement the VLR together with the MSC, so that the geographical area controlled by the MSC corresponds to that controlled by the VLR, thus simplifying the signalling requirement. Note that the MSC contains no information about particular mobile stations—this information is stored in the location registers.

Figure 8.12 illustrates how two registers (*e.g.*, HLR and VLR) swap database information as a mobile user (*i.e.*, *mobile station*, MS) moves from one network to another. For instance, assume that a network user (*i.e.*, Mobile Station in Fig. 8.12) is registered with 'Network #1' as its service-provider, which becomes its 'home register'. In this instance, the information pertaining to the network user (*e.g.*, account number, name, address, authentication and identification codes, etc) is held in its 'home register'. Immediately the mobile unit crosses to another network, it is assigned a *visiting location register* (VLR) by Network #2. Once transaction is completed as recorded by the 'foreign register' in Network #2, the details of such transaction are then transferred to mobile unit's home register (HLR) in Network #1. At the overlap, network #1 prepares to hand over the mobile user to network #2 fulfilling the network's obligation to providing service continuity. More is said about *handover* (also called *handoff*) in section 8.2.3.3 below.

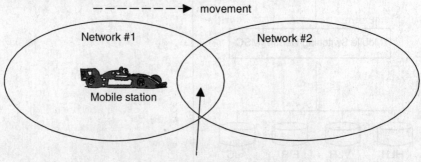

Fig. 8.12. An illustration of HRL and VLR for a mobile station traversing two networks

The *authentication centre* (AuC) is a protected database that stores a copy of the secret key stored in each subscriber's SIM card, which is used for authentication and encryption over the radio channel. AuC is associated with the HLR to protect each subscriber from unauthorised access. New generation authentication protocol allows for time privacy as well as subscriber authenticity. The *equipment identity register* (EIR) is a database that contains a list of all valid mobile equipment on the network, where each mobile station is identified by its IMEI (*International Mobile Equipment Identity*). In the case of a mobile station reported stolen or found incompatible with the networks approved item, an IMEI is marked as invalid.

8.2.3.2 *Mobile Switching Centre*

Mobile Switching Centre (MSC) is the network switch—like a switching node of the *public telephone network*—which directs traffic around the network between a mobile station and landline, or between two mobile stations. An MSC is usually placed in the population centres but not necessarily associated with every cluster of cells. More is said about radio cells later in section 8.2.3.3.

As seen in Fig. 8.13, an MSC provides the interface between the public telephone network (PSTN or ISDN), the base station and a mobile station. Typically, an MSC is composed of a number of computer elements controlling switching functions, such as call control, data interfaces, and user databases. Together with the base station controller (BSC), an MSC manages radio resource, channel assignments, and handover services.

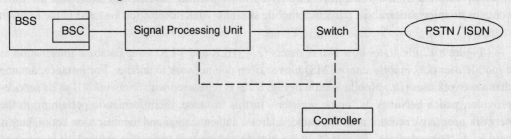

Fig. 8.13. Mobile Switching Centre (MSC)

The MSC call-controller takes the form of a software state machine implemented by microprocessors [Balston and Macario, 1993]. The call-controller's processing tasks vary markedly between manufactures. For example, some manufacturers have implemented channel allocation and BSS resource management at the MSC location, while others have executed these tasks at the BSS level. The MSC may be responsible for determining adjacent cells for measurement requests and for implementing the appropriate algorithm necessary to resolve the best cell for the target requesting handoff. If this were the case, the MSC would initiate and manage the sequence of events that terminates with the mobile station, MS, successfully arriving on the target cell.

Recent advances in technology have enabled MSCs to perform mobility management function as well as on-line maintenance features. The mobility management function regulates the registration of MSs as a function of position or time. The registration is needed to let the MSC know in which area the mobile service area an MS resides as well as cutting down on the number of cells used for paging a particular mobile. An MSC is regarded as an intelligent network because of its ability to manage subscribers' mobility correctly.

Ensuring the transmission of voice or data of a given quality over the radio link is only part of the function of a cellular mobile network. For any mobile devices to be able to roam seamlessly nationally and internationally, it would require that there exist registration, authentication, call routing, and location updating functions and are standardized in the traversing networks. Also, the fact that the geographical area covered by the network is divided into cells necessitates the implementation of a handover mechanism.

8.2.3.3 *Handover/Handoff*

Handover, or handoff as it is called in North America, is the switching of an on-going call to a different channel or cell. This process has been briefly touched in Section 8.2.2.1. Technically, handover is the process of automatically transferring a transaction in progress from one radio cell to another to avoid an adverse effect of users movement. For example, when a mobile user is moving outside the beam coverage or radio cell, like the illustration depicted in Fig 8.12, the call is handed over to the next beam. For call setup via order wire, each base station constantly monitors the strength of the modulated signals it is receiving from each user or subscriber. When the quality of this signal falls below certain pre-assigned norms (or values) because the direct path signal may have been attenuated, or the cellular user is moving outside the beam coverage, the *base station transceiver* (BTS) sends a request to the centralised switching centre asking it to attempt a handover. The BTS is the entity corresponding to one site communicating with one or multiple mobile stations (MSs). Usually, the BTS will have an antenna with several radio transceivers, each communicating on one radio frequency. The BTS antenna is usually located in the barocentre (centre of the radio cell) of the service area; see Fig. 8.14. A radio cell corresponds to the coverage area of one transmitter or a collection of transmitters. Simplified abstract shapes such as a hexagon or a circle often represent radio cells. More is said about radio cell in section 8.2.3.5.

The link-level signalling on the radio-channels is interpreted in the BTS, whereas most of the higher-level signalling is forwarded to the BSC and mobile station controller (MSC). The switch then automatically asks each adjoining base station to scan the frequency being used, and then report the quality of the signal it is picking. If a substantial improvement can be made, the switch automatically orders a handover. The switching over from one BTS to another as the abutting cell boundary is crossed is known as a *hard handoff* or *hard handover*, depicted in Fig. 8.14(*a*).

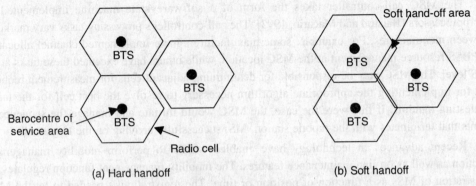

Fig. 8.14. Handoff techniques

Typically, instead of radio cells abutting as in Fig. 8.14(*a*), the radio cells can be arranged to overlap as in Fig. 8.14(*b*). In the situation of overlapping radio cells of Fig. 8.14(*b*), the system does not switch immediately from one BTS to another as the boundary is crossed. Instead, it makes use of both BTSs simultaneously (*i.e.*, while in the overlapping area), effectively making before breaking handoff. This process of handing over traffic is called a soft handover or soft handoff.

Handoff process is critical to system performance: it helps to avoid 'dropped' calls. In the case of soft handing-off, it helps to fill in any coverage 'gaps' and reduces the probability of dropped calls.

8.2.3.4 *Handoff Algorithm*

The preceding discussion has shown that either the mobile or the MSC—as a means of traffic load balancing, can initiate handovers. Traditional handoff algorithms are closely tied in with power control [Balston and Macario, 1993], based on received signal strength comparisons, and involves mobile terminals just moving from one base station to another within the same access network. This type of handoff is called *horizontal* handoff or *intrasystem* handoff [Akyildiz et al., 2004]. Current wireless networks are evolving, with the expectation of meeting future demands, including ability to coordinate services within a diverse-network environment. This process of seamless handoff is called *vertical* handoff or *intersystem* handoff. In the current 3G+ wireless networks, mobile terminals are envisioned to be equipped with multiple interfaces to establish connections with different types of wireless access networks. Thus, a handoff algorithm should meet both power budget requirement and seamless coordination, as well as meeting monetary cost, offered services, network conditions, and user preferences. Seamless vertical handoff decision algorithm is maturing. Readers interested in understanding the structure of these two types of handoff are advised to consult the literature including Balston and Macario (1993) and Akyildiz et al. (2004).

8.2.3.5 *Radio Cells and Location Areas*

In a cellular system, the coverage area of an operation is divided into radio cells. A *radio cell* corresponds to the coverage area of one transmitter or a collection of transmitters, whose size is determined by the intensity of the power radiated by the transmitter or a collection of transmitters. The frequency band allocated to the system is distributed over a group of cells that form a coverage area. Allotted frequency can be reused or repeated at a distance, *d*, several radio-cells away; a distance considered sufficient to avoid interference from adjoining cells, see Fig. 8.15. An

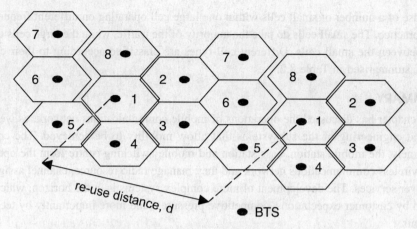

Fig. 8.15. Tessellated clusters of cells. (Adapted from: Kolawole, 2002)

inquiring reader should consult Kolawole (2002) to learn more on the acceptable conditions for frequency reuse without encountering interference from adjoining radio cells.

A *location* area corresponds to the area controlled by one MSC. As a mobile subscriber or user migrates from one location to another, his/her mobile unit, MS, would need to perform a location update by registering its presence in the new area where signal strength is more pronounced. The migratory signal continuity is possible by successfully handling over across cell boundaries. These cells could be a combination of small and large ones with the larger ones partly or wholly enveloping the smaller ones: an example is Fig. 8.16, which shows a form of radio cells configuration within a location area.

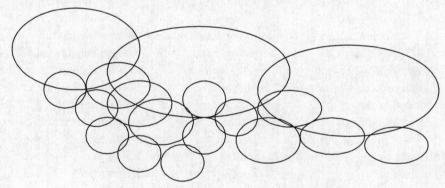

Fig. 8.16. Another form of radio cells arrangement

Table 8.2. Cells: type, location, and dimension

Cell Type	Antenna Location	Cell Size (km)
Large macrocell	Above rooftop level	3.0–30
Small macrocell	Above rooftop level	1.0–3.0
Microcell	At rooftop level	0.0–1.0
Picocell	Below rooftop level	0.0–0.1
Nanocell	Below rooftop level	0.00–0.01

The use of a number of small cells within one large cell operating on different frequencies is typical in practice. The small cells do take the majority of the traffic, while the large cells cover all the gaps between the small cells. Different cell-types are classified according to their coverage dimension, summarised in Table 8.2.

8.3 SUMMARY

This chapter has discussed the operations of mobile communications network, as well as the process and engineering of the subsystems that allow mobility to be achieved. The combined entities namely, the mobile station, base station and mobile switching centre form the operational path of a wireless communications network and they manage radio resource, channel assignments, and handover services. The development of more complex systems is in the horizon, which would be dictated by customer expectations, competitive pressures, and more importantly by technology requirements.

QUESTIONS

1. You have been commissioned to develop a wireless communications network for a State. Develop a blueprint and highlight the issues to consider.
2. Write a program that is capable of handling calls handover from one sector to another and between networks.
3. The issue of excessive radiation plays an important role in radio-communications, and given the limited radio spectrum resource, what type of antenna systems would you recommend for a wireless network? Discuss how the radiation concern can be mitigated?
4. Why do networks have far fewer mobile radio channels than users?

9

TRAFFIC ANALYSIS

The previous chapters have dealt with network underlying technology, architecture, and noted applicable standards. What needs to be considered is whether the network can support the traffic, which the users and applications generate. Probabilistic concepts are used to investigate traffic interaction with a network to providing quantitative measures of the network performance. An application of probabilistic systems analysis concepts forms the theme of this chapter.

All networks concentrate. With the exception of a small and dedicated network, most networks have not been designed to handle all traffic that could arise at the same time. So, nearly all networks are built to support the sum of all traffic up to a certain level of the network's capacity. Associated with the capacity is a *Grade of Service*, *GoS*—the probability of the offered traffic exceeding the capacity, or *Quality of Service*, QoS—a set of quality requirements on the collective behavior of one or more objects on all aspects of a connection including time to provide service, voice quality, echo, loss, reliability, etc. GoS is calculated from the perspective of the resource and not from the perspective of the request. The parameters, GoS and QoS, have been summarily discussed in Chapters 2 (section 2.4.2) and 3 (section 3.6). Furthermore, the analytical basis on which the expressions in Section 3.6 were obtained is further discussed in this chapter.

The basic assumption is that traffic (telephone calls, text, or graphic data) arises from each particular source with certain probability. The traffic at the base station level involves handovers across radio cells. The quality of service is enhanced if the rate of breakdown during a transaction is small. Queue theory can be exploited to study the performance and processing of calls and data in the networks at the *base station* and *mobile switching centre* levels because the traffic that arrives at any one node in the networks can encounter either some or no processing (*e.g.*, the traffic can be buffered in and out without delay), or some delay (or blockage) due to existing traffic being dealt with before the new traffic can be processed. Whilst attempting to exploit queue theory, this chapter bypasses mathematically rigorous proofs and relies instead on simpler intuitive explanations. Readers wanting to know the theoretical development of Queue theory from a communications perspective should consult Massey (2002).

9.1 QUEUE THEORY

Queue theory, more generally, is concerned with the mathematical modelling and analysis of systems that provide service to random demands. A queue model is an abstract description of such a system. In most cases, a queue model represents two things:

(a) the system physical configuration—by specifying the number and arrangement of the *servers*, which provide the service; and

(b) the stochastic nature of the demands—by specifying the variability in the *arrival process* and in the *service process*. The stochastic nature of the demands can be probabilistic or statistical.

It could be said in general that queue systems are characterized by the input process and the services and queue disciplines. In practice, queuing processes and disciplines are often complicated, which may not be amenable to analysis. To obtain a meaningful result, therefore, it may be useful to rely on simpler memoryless, single queue models, which may be amenable to analysis.

Consider a single-server queue of Fig. 9.1 capable of handling calls and/or packets of data that arrive randomly at an average rate λ per second, and queue up for service in the buffer, or channel, at an average rate μ per second. In the ensuing development the word 'calls' applies equally to calls and/or packets of data.

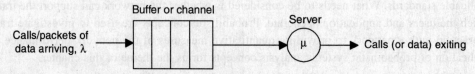

Fig. 9.1. A representation of a single queue

To familiarise the reader with the commonly used shorthand notations for single queue models in the literature, we begin by discussing the sequence of notation representation. A shorthand notation for single queue models that describes the arrival process, service distribution, the number of servers and the buffer size (waiting room) is as follows:

arrival process / service distribution / number of servers / waiting room

Suppose the queue model is characterised by a stochastic arrival process (*e.g.*, Markov, Poisson or equivalent), service-time statistic (*e.g.*, exponential 'M', or deterministic 'D') infinite number of servers, and unknown waiting rooms, then the queue model can be denoted by M/M/∞/*). The *fourth* position is used for the number of buffer places in addition to the number of servers and it is usually not used if the waiting room is unlimited.

The simplest canonical delay, time-varying rates model queue is denoted by M/M/1 queue, which has Poisson arrivals, exponentially distributed holding times, a single server (*e.g.*, first in first out, FIFO), and an infinite buffer. For l servers and deterministic or constant service time, the queue notation becomes M/D/l.

The queue model is one of the fundamental models of teletraffic engineering where the "customers" are 'telephone calls' (which can wait until the necessary resources are available) and the "servers" are "lines or trunks", and when the blocked calls are cleared from the system and they are "lost" calls.

The traffic intensity [Erlang, 1917] or offered traffic flow to the base station may be expressed:

$$A = \frac{\lambda}{\mu} \quad \text{(Erlang)} \tag{9.1}$$

For a single-server queue, as A in (9.1) approaches and exceeds unity, the region of congestion is encountered; time delays of data or calls in the buffer begin to increase rapidly, and the calls or packets arriving are blocked from entering the buffer more often. To quantify the time delay, blocking performance and traffic throughput (*i.e.*, actual value of traffic that gets through the network) and their connection with packet rate capacity and the size of the buffer needs to be investigated. These variables are readily determined once the probability of state, P, at the queue is specified.

Suppose there are k calls present in the queue, where $k = 0, 1, 2, 3, ..., m$. The probability of a new call arriving in time dt is $(\lambda_k dt)$ and the probability of a call terminating is $(\mu_k dt)$. So, the probability of simultaneous calls P_k present at time $(t + dt)$ may be written as

$$P_k (t + dt) = P_k (t) [(1 - \lambda_k dt)(1 - \mu_k dt)] + P_{k-1} (t) \lambda_{k-1} dt + P_{k+1} (t) \mu_{k+1} dt \quad (9.2a)$$

Alternatively, $\dfrac{dP_k}{dt} = - (\lambda_k + \mu_k) P_k + \lambda_{k-1} P_{k-1} + \mu_{k+1} P_{k+1}$ \quad (9.2b)

The expression (9.2b) needs to be solved to find the time variation of the simultaneous calls probability, $P_k (t)$. For the sake of tidiness, the time (t) is omitted in the preceding development. Equation (9.2b) is assumed to reach a steady-state condition as time goes on. So, at a stationary state,

$$(\lambda_k + \mu_k) P_k = \lambda_{k-1} P_{k-1} + \mu_{k+1} P_{k+1} \quad (9.3)$$

The left hand of this expression represents the rate of *leaving* state k, given the system in state k with probability P_k. Whereas the right hand terms represent the rate of *entering* state k from either state $(k - 1)$ or $(k + 1)$. The steady state diagram arising from (9.3) is shown in Fig. 9.2. Transitional rates λ and μ are appended to the arrival and departure nodes because of the rates distributions have been assumed Poissonian. If the system is in state '0'; it is empty, and it can only move to state '1' due to arrival.

Fig. 9.2. State transitional diagram

By assuming that

$$\mu_0 = 0, \text{ so that a call cannot end if none exists, and}$$
$$\lambda_M = 0, \text{ so that a call cannot arise if } M \text{ calls already exist,}$$

some limiting equations can be written, thus:

$$\mu_1 P_1 = \lambda_0 P_0 \qquad\qquad (\lambda_{-1} = 0) \quad (9.4)$$
$$\mu_M P_M = \lambda_{M-1} P_{M-1} \qquad\qquad (\mu_{M+1} = 0) \quad (9.5)$$

Considering (9.3) through to (9.5), the solution to (9.2b) can be expressed as

$$P_k = P_0 \left(\frac{\prod\limits_{l=0}^{k-1} \lambda_i}{\prod\limits_{l=1}^{k} \mu_i} \right) \qquad k = 1, 2, ..., M \quad (9.6a)$$

$$P_k = 0 \qquad\qquad k > M \quad (9.6b)$$

where Π is the symbol for the product. One recognises from statistics that the sum of probabilities P_k must equal to unity. So,

$$P_0 + P_0 \sum_{k=1}^{M} \left(\frac{\prod\limits_{l=0}^{k-1} \lambda_i}{\prod\limits_{l=1}^{k} \mu_i} \right) = 1 \quad (9.7)$$

Suppose one deals with a large number of terminals, servers, channels, etc., then the calls' arrival rate λ_k remains constant (*i.e.*, λ) even if the channels are already busy or not. Of course, this constraint does not affect the probability of arrival of new calls. Also, if each call's duration is assumed to have an exponential distribution, one can assume that $\mu_k = \mu k$ [Purser, 1987]. One recognises that the average call duration is also $T_d = \dfrac{1}{\mu}$ and substituting this in (9.6) and (9.7) to obtain

$$P_k = P_0 \frac{(\lambda T_d)^k}{k!} \tag{9.8}$$

with the symbol '!' denoting factorial. Note that $x! = 1.2.3.4, ..., x$, if $x = 5$ for example, $5! = 1.2.3.4.5 = 120$. Also note that $0! = 1$.

$$P_0 \left(1 + \sum_{k=1}^{M} \frac{(\lambda T_d)^k}{k!} \right) = 1 \tag{9.9}$$

Rearranging (9.1) as $A = \dfrac{\lambda}{\mu} = \lambda T_d$, and substituting it in (9.9), we have

$$P_0 = \frac{1}{1 + \displaystyle\sum_{k=1}^{M} \frac{A^k}{k!}} = \frac{1}{\displaystyle\sum_{k=0}^{M} \frac{A^k}{k!}} \tag{9.10}$$

noting that for $M = 0$, $0! = 1$ and $A^0 = 1$.

Substitution of (9.10) in (9.8) gives the *Erlang-B formula* for the probability of k simultaneous calls, thus

$$P_k = \frac{\dfrac{A^k}{k!}}{\displaystyle\sum_{i=0}^{M} \frac{A^i}{i!}} \tag{9.11}$$

This expression may be written in terms of traffic congestion, $B(M, A)$:

$$B(M, A) = \frac{\dfrac{A^M}{M!}}{\displaystyle\sum_{i=0}^{M} \frac{A^i}{i!}} \tag{9.12}$$

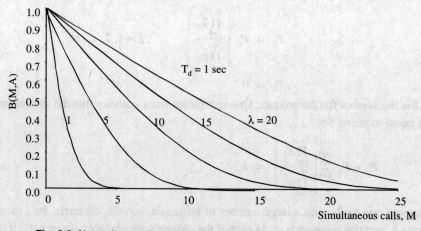

Fig. 9.3. Network capacity required to support fully occupied channel.

The expression (9.12) is the probability of a network capable of supporting M simultaneous calls being fully occupied, given that the offered traffic flow is A and assuming that any calls in excess of M are rejected (*i.e.*, the blocked-calls-lost assumption [Purser, 1987]). Equation (9.12) forms the cornerstone for evaluating the *Grade of Service* (GoS) of traffic networks—used in chapter 3, section 3.6. A plot of (9.12) is shown in Fig. 9.3.

As demonstrated by the non-linear curves in Fig. 9.3, the low traffic flows require more capacity to handle the flows in proportion to that of high traffic flows. It is possible to deduce that in order to maintain a GoS requires the system to be lightly loaded.

Example 9.1: A group of 4 channels is offered a traffic intensity of 1.5 Erlang. Assume that call arrivals are having a Poisson process, and for an average holding time of 1.8 minutes, calculate

(a) the average number of calls per hour

(b) the probabilities that (i) no call arrives and (ii) two calls will be blocked.

If the channels and traffic intensity increased to 25 and 15 Erlang respectively, calculate

(c) the call blocking probability and

(d) the probability of a free channel.

Solution: (a) From the offered traffic A given by (9.1), calculate the average number of calls per hour

$$\lambda = 1.5*60/1.8 = 50 \text{ calls/hr}$$

(b) If one represents k as the number of call arrivals within a time interval t to have an average arrival rate λ, then the probability of the arrival of exactly k messages can be written as

$$P_k(t) = \frac{(t\lambda)^k}{k!} e^{-\lambda t} \qquad\qquad k = 0, 1, ..., n \qquad (9.13)$$

Using this expression, the probability that (i) no call arrives, P_0 (1.8), is

$$P_0(1.8) = \frac{(1.5)^0}{0!} e^{-1.5} = 0.223$$

(ii) The probability that 2 calls were blocked is obtained using (9.12)

$$k = 2, M = 4$$
$$P_n = 0.2558$$

(c) Probability of blocking channel: using (9.12)

$$B(25, 15) = \frac{\dfrac{15^{25}}{25!}}{\displaystyle\sum_{i=0}^{25} \dfrac{15^i}{i!}} = 0.005$$

(d) Probability of a free channel: this case is the same as if 24 channels were busy, hence

$$B(24, 15) = \frac{\dfrac{15^{24}}{24!}}{\displaystyle\sum_{i=0}^{24} \dfrac{15^i}{i!}} = 0.008$$

Expression (9.12) applies to *any* distribution of service times; this mathematically surprising and practically important result is an example of the phenomenon of *insensitivity* [Cooper, 1990].

And, this formula (9.12) is hard to calculate directly when M and A are large, but is easy to calculate numerically using the following iterative scheme [Cooper, 1990]:

$$B(s, A) = \frac{AB(s-1, A)}{s + AB(s-1, A)} \qquad s = 1, 2, ..., M; B(0, A) = 1 \qquad (9.14)$$

9.2   TRAFFIC MODELS AT BASE STATION LEVEL

The preceding queue theory can also be utilised to investigate the performance of traffic at the base station (BS) level, in particular, where the cells are large (*e.g.*, macrocells) because handovers between BSs are relatively rare and the channel (buffer) holding time, T_{ch}, may approximate the call duration T_d. This assumption may be inadequate in the case of microcells where there may be fast fluctuations in the traffic intensity. As a result, both microcell and macrocell models need to be developed.

9.2.1   Macrocell Model

Since the cells are large and handovers between base stations are scarce, one can assume that the number k of *mobile stations*, MSs, per cell is so much greater than the number of BS channels, N; (*i.e.*, $k >> N$). As a result, the number of users (k) may be approximated as infinite. The probability P_N of a new traffic being denied (or blocked) must be significantly greater than the probability P_h of an existing call being forced to terminate due to handover failure between two BSs. Hence, using (9.12), the probability of a call attempt being blocked is expressed as

$$P_N = \frac{\dfrac{A^N}{N!}}{\displaystyle\sum_{j=0}^{N} \dfrac{A^j}{j!}} = B(N, A) \qquad (9.15)$$

Steele (1992) noted that the call requests arriving at the BS, and being cleared by the network, are independent events. Hence, the blocked traffic C_b may be expressed

$$C_b = AP_n \qquad (9.16a)$$

And the net arrival rate, or *throughput*, ρ be expressed by

$$\rho = \lambda (1 - P_N) \qquad (9.16b)$$

Consequently, the net traffic C_n carried by a base station is

$$C_n = A (1 - P_n) = \frac{\rho}{\mu} \qquad (9.17)$$

Example 9.2: Suppose in a busy hour there are 6000 mobile stations, each generating 0.015 Erlang. The mobile stations are connected to a base station capable of handling 110 simultaneous traffics. Calculate the offered traffic, grade of service, and the channel load factor.

Solution: $N = 110$

(1) Offered traffic, $A = 6000*0.015 = 90$ Erlang

(2) Using either (9.12) or (9.15), the probability of full loading, or Grade of Service, equals

$$B(110, 90) = \frac{\dfrac{90^{110}}{110!}}{\displaystyle\sum_{i=0}^{110} \dfrac{90^i}{i!}} = 0.005 \text{ or } 0.5\%$$

(3) Since 0.5% of the traffic is lost, using (9.17) the average traffic flow supported by the BS:

$$C_n = (1 - 0.005)*90 = 89.55 \text{ Erlang}$$

(4) Channel load factor: $\dfrac{C_n}{N} = \dfrac{89.55}{110} = 0.8141 \text{ or } 81.41\%$

9.2.2 Microcell Model

The microcell model considers small cells where handovers between mobile stations, MSs, are frequent. Because of this frequency, applying the queue theory is much more difficult [Dolil et. al, 1989; Steele and Nofal, 1992; Chlebus, 1996]. Although, the number of channels 'N' and the number of MSs 'k' in both the microcells and macrocells cases may not be significantly different: it would be desirable to consider the number of microcells in the BS as N_c. The offered traffic A (9.1) to a base station is the same as in the macrocell situation. Let the inter-arrival time of calls be denoted by T_{in}. If A is very small and the blocking probability approaches zero, then the average offered traffic per user (terminal or server) β can be expressed as

$$\beta = \frac{A}{k} \tag{9.18a}$$

or $$\beta = \frac{1}{\mu T_{in}} = \frac{\alpha}{\mu} \tag{9.18b}$$

Engset (1918) expressed β in terms of (9.1) and (9.15) to give

$$\beta = \frac{A}{M - A(1 - P_N)} \tag{9.18c}$$

Suppose i number of BS channels is in use out of total N_c, then the following expressions may be written:

(a) Average call arrival as

$$\lambda_i = \left(\frac{M - i}{T_{in}} \right) = \alpha (M - i) \tag{9.19a}$$

(b) Traffic exiting rates as

$$\mu_i = i\mu \tag{9.19b}$$

By using the independent relation, it is apparent that the probability of N_c channels—when considered busy—may be expressed as

$$P_{N_c} = \frac{\left(\dfrac{k}{N_c} \right) \beta^{N_c}}{\sum\limits_{j=0}^{N_c} \left(\dfrac{k}{j} \right) \beta^j} \tag{9.20}$$

which, in comparison with (9.15), is a fraction of the time when all channels are in use. Note that

$$\left(\frac{k}{N_c} \right) = \frac{k!}{(k - N_c)! \, N_c!}$$

From (9.20), it is easy to express the probability that a call is attempted when all channels are busy by

$$P_{att} = \frac{\left(\dfrac{k-1}{N_c}\right)\beta^{N_c}}{\sum\limits_{j=0}^{N_c}\left(\dfrac{k-1}{j}\right)\beta^j} \tag{9.21}$$

For fast fluctuations of traffic intensity due to frequently making handovers by mobile stations, one can confidently assume that new and handover traffic streams are Poissonian and channel holding times are exponentially distributed. In practice, the distribution is not exactly Poisson but close. If the time between successive arrivals is represented by τ, then for Poisson distribution, the probability density function $f_\tau(\tau)$ is given by

$$f_\tau(\tau) = \lambda e^{-\lambda t} \qquad \tau \geq 0 \tag{9.22}$$

A simple calculation shows that the mean value $E(\tau)$ of (9.22) is

$$E(\tau) = \int_0^\infty \tau f_\tau(\tau)\,d\tau = \frac{1}{\lambda} \tag{9.23}$$

Denote the mean channel holding time by T_{ch}, the mean handover time by T_h, and the mean fresh or new call time by T_n. Given that the mobile stations frequently make handovers, the channel holding time T_{ch} would be far less than the call duration T_d. Also, the mean total arrival rate λ_t will be the sum of the mean fresh call rate λ_n and mean handover request rate λ_h, formalised as

$$\lambda_t = \lambda_n + \lambda_h \tag{9.24}$$

while the mean channel holding time T_{ch} is given by [Steele, 1992]

$$T_{ch} = \gamma_n T_n + \gamma_h T_h \tag{9.25a}$$

where $\quad \gamma_n = \dfrac{\lambda_n}{\lambda_t}\quad$ ratio of carried new call rate to the total arrival rate $\tag{9.25b}$

$$\gamma_h = 1 - \gamma_n = \text{ratio of carried handover rate to the new call rate} \tag{9.25c}$$

From the preceding equations, the traffic carried by the microcell BS is expressed:

$$C_{mic} = A_t(1 - P_{N_c}) \tag{9.26}$$

with $A_t = \dfrac{\lambda_t}{\mu N_c}$. Equation (9.26) is valid for the case where no priority assignment of channels is provided for handover requests. Steele (1992) noted that a method of decreasing the probability of handover failure is to use a macrocell to overspill a cluster of microcells. In that situation, the traffic carried by one macrocell BS may be expressed by

$$Cmac = A_k(1 - P_{N_f}) \tag{9.27}$$

with $A_k = \dfrac{\lambda}{\mu k}$ and where $P_{N_f} = 1 - P_N$, which is the probability of handover failure in the macrocell.

The network average utilisation ζ can be written as

$$\zeta = \frac{C_{mic} + C_{mac}}{N + N_c} \tag{9.28}$$

The total traffic carried by the network may be written as

$$C_T = NC_{mac} + N_c C_{mic}$$

If the number of channels supported by the macrocells BS is small compared to that carried by the microcells BS, the spectral efficiency, η, may be written as

$$\eta = \frac{C_T}{B_x A_x} \qquad \text{Erlang/Hz-m}^2 \qquad (9.29)$$

where B_x and A_x correspond to available bandwidth allocated to the network and total area covered by the network. Alternatively,

$$\eta \cong \frac{\zeta}{B_c A_{sec} N_{sec}} \qquad \text{Erlang/Hz-m}^2 \qquad (9.30)$$

where N_{sec}, B_c, and A_{sec} correspond to the number of microcells per cluster, the equivalent bandwidth per channel, and average area of each microcell in the cluster.

The implication of (9.30) is that for high η, the microcell area A_{sec} and deployed channel bandwidth, B_c, as well as the number of microcells per cluster N_{sec}, should be small. Of course, B_c depends on the modulation and multiple access technique used (*e.g.*, *Frequency Division Multiple Access*, FDMA, *Time Division Multiple Access*, TDMA, and *Code Division Multiple Access*, CDMA). An advantage of CDMA is that it meets all the requirements outlined for high η, in this case, $N_{sec} = 1$. The reader, who desires a deeper knowledge and more rigorous analysis of the multiple access techniques, is referred to the author's *Satellite Communication Engineering* (Marcel Dekker, 2002). It might be tempted to increase the network average utilisation ζ; the number of channels must be decreased. However, if the *grade of service*, GoS, is to be maintained, the blocking probability must remain low. Consequently, it is more appropriate to increase the number of channels, which, in turn, will increase ζ and therefore η for the same blocking probability.

9.2.3 Risk Analysis

The previous sections have concentrated on traffic analysis and the measurement of system performance. These sections have not however considered the effect of an intruder rerouting the traffic causing significant delay or preventing it from delivering the traffic load to their intended destination at all. The design of base stations should speculate about associated technical difficulties, resourcing, scheduling, traffic pattern identification, etc. These give rise to uncertainty of events or risks that must be managed in order to limit the impact on the system and network performance. It is clear therefore that to abate a risk one has to:

- Reduce the likelihood of the unwanted event occurring, and
- Reduce the adverse impact should that event occur.

Despite best intentions of encryption, an eavesdropper can identify traffic patterns, which can divulge information about the operation mode of the base stations. Presenting "constant" traffic pattern as well as inserting dummy traffic can prevent traffic analysis by any intruders with malicious intent. This raises the need for traffic algorithm optimisation and access control protocol.

Network routing protocols are vulnerable to attacks thereby subverting the network's execution flow towards a desired malicious procedure and/or subverting routing metrics. Network vulnerability stems from misapplication of cryptographic primitives, careless protocol or system call implementations, or lack of shared infrastructure and dynamic relationships between the nodes in the network. The control mechanism should be robust enough to ensure rapid reconfiguration of the subnetwork once a violation has been identified. The access control protocol must be optimally adaptive and easily verifiable, and must be capable of enforcing three main security goals namely: authentication, data integrity and network infrastructure protection.

9.3 SUMMARY

Measuring the rate of breakdown during a conversation or transmission is a way of assessing the traffic performance of any network, particularly at the Base Station (BS) and/or Mobile Switching Centre (MSC) level. In this chapter, the probabilistic systems analysis concepts have been applied to investigate the network throughput, grade of service, the average traffic flow supportable by a BS and/or MSC, and channel load factor. The chapter concludes by looking at the risk factor and what is needed to prevent network's vulnerability to exploitation by passive or active measures.

QUESTIONS

1. For an infinite-server system operating at 85% utilization, what fraction of customers will wait longer than one average service time?

2. A study to the handover requests found that 10% failed for 1200 calls. If the network operates at 80% utilization, calculate the average area of radio-cell and its spectral efficiency.

3. Suppose a network's traffic is offered 8 erlangs of Poisson distribution to 10 servers. What proportion of the arrivals will be blocked?

4. Write a program that implements (9.14), and verify that $B(1, 0.8) = 0.4444$, $B(100, 80) = 0.003992$, and $B(1000, 800) = 10^{-12}$.

5. The total traffic carried by the network is 1,430,000 calls per hour with an allocated bandwidth of 9.5 kHz. A study shows that in a single hour, an 85% utilisation is observed by the base station. Calculate the area covered by the base station. What sort of antenna would you advise for the station?

10

NANOTECHNOLOGY

Nanotechnology is an area of technology that is generating some excitement particularly in engineering and sciences. While the potentials derivable from nanotechnology may be overstated, or understated, not much has been proved to lead to a large-scale benefit; yet. Nevertheless, science and engineering envisioned a high-order of magnitude breakthroughs in the performance of systems and products. This chapter explains the concept of nanotechnology and its potential from the standpoint of application to telecommunications discipline, particularly the way we currently handle and transport telecommunication devices and information.

10.1 WHAT IS NANOTECHNOLOGY?

Nanotechnology is the science of the extremely tiny particles—called nanoparticles—on the scale of approximately 1 to 100 nm. The prefix *nano* is a Greek word for dwarf, something small. As a prefix for a unit of time or length, it refers to a nanosecond (ns) or nanometre (nm), which means one billionth of that unit. Thus, a nanosecond is 10^{-9} second and nanometre is 10^{-9} metre. To virtualise how small a nanometre is; it is about one eighty thousandth the width (w_h) of a human hair (*i.e.*, $1.25*10^{-5} w_h$).

Nanoparticles are the building blocks of nanotechnology. The term 'nanotechnology' encompasses such a wide range of tools, techniques, and potential applications requiring an integration of a variety of disciplines such as: chemistry, physics, mechanics, materials, electronic and measurement technologies. In functional form, nanotechnology is the engineering of functional systems at the molecular level. From the standpoint of application, nanotechnology is the design, characterisation, production and application of structures, devices and systems by controlling shape and size at nanometre scale. Nanotechnology is widely seen as having huge potential to impact on a wide range of applications in many industries in the medium- and long term: not only to boost the competitiveness of traditional industries but also to create new products and enable orders of magnitude breakthroughs in the performance of the products. The following lends support to this optimism.

1. The fundamental building blocks of nature, atoms and molecules, have dimensions in the nanoscale range. For example, many water molecules can easily occupy a sphere of 1 nm in diameter. The way molecules assemble into larger, supramolecular entities on the nanoscale determines important material properties, such as electrical, optical, and mechanical properties. By controlling the molecular structure on the nanometre-scale range, it is possible to design new materials and devices with specific properties for applications capable of being designed for use in a wide range of electronics, chemicals, communications, and consumer products.

2. When particle sizes are reduced to the nanoscale, the ratio of surface area to volume increases dramatically. And, different properties, or characteristics are formed, and

surprisingly, behave differently. If a bulk material is broken down into nanosized particles, many of the bulk material's properties often change. For instance, by breaking a lump of gold, yellowy in colour, into nanosize chunks (in the 10 to 100 nanometre range), the gold changes colour to appearing reddish. Whilst the chemical composition of the gold has not changed, the physical and chemical properties have changed because more surface area of the material has been opened up and exposed. This explains why very small particles are staggeringly reactive: the more surface area, the more catalytic action, with the potential to speed up almost all physical and manufacturing processes. Nanosized materials can be stronger or lighter, or conduct heat or electricity in a different way. They can be grown like crystals, virtually atom by atom.

Nature has consistently performed this assembly (*i.e.*, growing things molecule by molecule) creating sophisticated molecular machinery that supports our life on earth. Nanotechnology attempts to emulate nature. Thus, nanotechnology can be described as the engineering of functional systems at the molecular scale that covers both current work and concepts that are more advanced.

10.2 CONSTRUCTION, APPLICATION AND TIMESCALE

Conceptualisation leads to development and the time taken to reach construction stage varies markedly. It is difficult to predict the precise timescale for which different nanotechnologies will become a reality. Nano-enhanced products already available; examples include computer chips that have nano-sized features etched onto their surface, or nanoparticles of titanium dioxide that have been added to some suntan lotions and cosmetics to reflect ultra-violet rays. But on a larger scale, it is expected that more products would be manufactured that are lighter, stronger, cleaner and less expensive, which could impact on many areas of life and systems including ultra-precision engineering and communications products. However, this type of nano-manufacturing has not yet begun in any substantial way and will take decades to mature.

Previous chapters have demonstrated how wireless technology has improved the way people communicate on the move, everywhere they go. Consumers are increasingly demanding: an example is the need to combine communication and computational nodes into a device allowing continuous access to work materials and friends regardless of the location and time of the day. This requirement demands versatility, faster data transfer and responses, lower energy consumption, smaller devices, and larger data storage facility, which nanotechnology is envisioned to lead the way in meeting this goal.

Meeting this goal would require an appropriate approach to controlling and fabricating integrated complex systems and associated devices on the nanoscale. In general, there are two approaches to the design of complex integrated systems, namely, *bottom-up* and *top-down* techniques. The use of *bottom-up* and *top-down* techniques in fabrication is shown in Fig. 10.1.

In the *bottom-up* technique, as in Fig. 10.1(*a*), attempts to build from the ground up creating molecules on a surface and then allowing them to assemble into larger structures. This technique involves the building of structures, atom-by-atom or molecule-by-molecule. The wide variety of approaches towards achieving this goal can be split into three categories: chemical synthesis (using programmable chemistry as the basis of a manufacturing system, for example); self-assembly (a self-contained factory that includes machinery to build all its machinery, for example); and positional assembly (for example, adding a few atoms at a time in programmable positions; thus shifting the complexity from the hardware to the software).

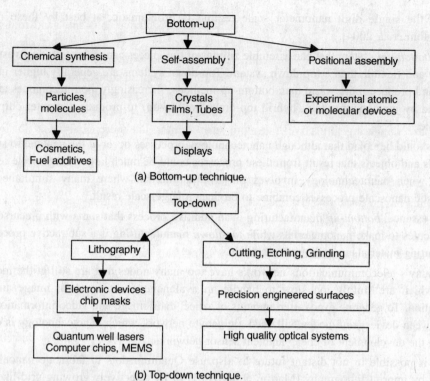

Fig. 10.1. The use of bottom-up and top-down techniques in manufacturing. (Courtesy: The Royal Society and The Royal Academy of Engineering, 2004)

Royalsociety (2004) noted that positional assembly (with its many practical drawbacks as a manufacturing tool) is the only technique in which single atoms or molecules can be placed deliberately one-by-one. More typically, large numbers of atoms, molecules or particles are used or created by chemical synthesis, and then arranged through naturally occurring processes into a desired structure.

Unlike the bottom-up manufacturing technologies where processes are controlled by self-assembly, the process of manufacturing, using the top-down technique—as shown in Fig. 10.1(*b*), starts on the macro-scale (bigger building blocks) and proceeds to create fine features by processing the bulk on a fine scale (that is, etching, milling or machining a nanostructure from the bulk). Lithographic methods are capable of producing micron-sized features (for example printed circuits, computer chips and boards, compact discs, mobile phones, and *micro-electro-mechanical systems*, MEMS). MEMS is the integration of mechanical elements, sensors, actuators, and electronics on a common silicon substrate through microfabrication technology. In the MEMS context, lithography is typically the transfer of a pattern to a photosensitive material by selective exposure to a radiation source such as light. A photosensitive material changes its physical properties when exposed to a radiation source. Switching is a crucial function in any telecommunications networks. However, for future all-optical telecommunications networks, MEMS would play prominent role.

Top-down lithographic methods have yielded structures that possess seemingly arbitrary complexity from a wide range of materials and achieving fabrication success at the atomic scale, even in the single digit nanometer scale regime is problematic, at best by these methods [Awschalom et al, 2004].

A *bottom-up* system that can assemble zillions of tiny pieces can make a product vastly more intricate and flexible than a top-down system. Top-down systems are generally higher in energy usage, and produce more waste than bottom-up methods. Increasingly, both techniques are being exploited by juxtaposition (*i.e.*, hybrid top-down/bottom-up) to produce computer chips at the nanoscale.

It should be noted that although nanotechnology processes occur at the nanometre scale, the materials and objects that result from these processes could be much larger. Large-scale result can happen when nanotechnology involves massive parallelism where many simultaneous and synergistic nanoscale processes combine to produce a large-scale result.

In essence, *bottom-up* manufacturing is an additive process that starts with precursor atoms or molecules to make nanomaterials while *top-down* manufacturing is a subtractive process from bulk starting materials to make nanomaterials.

Today's telecommunications networks have too many nodes that are still at the megabyte-level, which are simply too slow to handle an avalanche of voice, data, image and video information. To generate ever-faster amounts of voice, data, image and video information within and between devices and nodes will need a gigabyte network which nanotechnology is enabling through the development of cheap ambient sensor networks.

It is possible in not distant future to also use Quantum dots to fabricate nanoelectronic devices by imprint lithography [Martini et al., 2001] or by selectively growing grid-like pattern [Nakamura et al., 2000].

Basically, a dot is a giant artificial atom made up of thousands of real atoms. Quantum dots can occur spontaneously in quantum well structures due to monolayer fluctuations in the well's thickness. A quantum well is a thin layer that confines particles in the dimension perpendicular to the layer surface but not restricted in the other dimensions. Self-assembled quantum dots nucleate spontaneously under certain conditions during molecular beam epitaxy when a material is grown on a substrate to which it is not lattice-matched. Epitaxy is the process of depositing a micron-sized thin layer of single crystal material over a single crystal substrate, usually through chemical vapour deposition.

Quantum dots may also be used to transfer information between components within devices at the speed of light, with each piece of information 'coded' by being a unique wavelength of light. Research studies are continuing to centre on quantum dot nanocomposite materials and associated devices to realising faster, cheaper, and more powerful optical telecommunication components.

10.3 RISK AND SAFETY CONSIDERATION

With any new technology, there is always a lingering doubt about its effect on human health and the environment. It could be argued that since nanomaterial is fixed or etched onto a larger object and therefore unable to stray into the environment, most current and future nanotechnologies would pose no new health or safety risks. However, concerns do exist about the possible impact of manufactured nanoparticles and nanotubes that are free to move around rather than being fixed or embedded into a bulk material. This concern echoes the various, vicious form of cancer caused by asbestos, including peritoneal mesothelioma, which manifests itself by inhaling or ingesting free asbestos fibres that damage the cells. Nanoparticles are free particles that could be inhaled, ingested or enter the body via the skin, and then cause damage to cells. Nanotubes, for example, are structurally similar to asbestos fibres, which can cause respiratory problems when inhaled in large amounts over long periods. Nanotubes occur in a variety of structures, lengths and diameters and sometimes form messy spaghetti-like tangles, which in not distant future orderly tubes with specified dimensions and properties could become a reality.

Should this concern impede advances in nanotechnology?

The author is of the opinion that some regulatory measures—including national and international legislative frameworks—be instituted that provide sufficient safeguard to the handling and disposition of nanoparticles, and concurrent research into potential hazards to keep pace with new developments. At present, almost nothing is known about the potential effects of free nanoparticles and nanotubes on the environment. But, it is possible that free nanoparticles and nanotubes could enter the food chain, and affect plants and animals. Until their effects are better understood, release of these particles into the environment should be minimised. It is also possible that nanotechnology could be potentially beneficial to the environment: through the use of nanomaterials, to create fuel cells and photovoltaic cells, or to remove heavy metals, cyanide and other substances that damage the environment.

In essence, research and development in nanotechnology should be directed toward understanding and creating improved materials, devices, and systems that exploit these new properties, as well as minimising the risks to the environment and human health.

10.4 SUMMARY

Nanoscience and nanotechnologies attempt to combine exciting areas of research and development at the interface between biology, material science, chemistry and physics. These emerging technologies are widely seen as having huge potential that would impact on a wide range of applications in many industries in the medium- and long term: not only to boost the competitiveness of traditional industries but also to create new products and enable orders of magnitude breakthroughs in the performance of the products. Fashioning these nanomaterials to our needs promises to advance the gigabyte network, or moving from microarrays toward smart nanoarrays antennae, or creating highly focused precision systems. The need to safeguard the environment as well as preventing adverse risks to human health should be paramount in the development and application of the nanotechnology.

QUESTIONS

1. Are nanoscience and nanotechnologies complementary? Explain your rationale.
2. Are the claims about benefits and risks of nanotechnologies real or overstated?
3. Which areas of telecommunications engineering do you think would gain most from these emerging technologies? Explain.
4. As a development engineer, what would you consider when embarking on manufacturing nanoproducts?

BIBLIOGRAPHY

Akyildiz, I., Xie, J. and Mohanty, S. (2004). A Survey of Mobility Management in Next-Generation All-IP-Based Wireless Systems. *IEEE Wireless Communications*, 11:4, 16–28.

Audestad, J.A. (1988). Network aspects of the GSM system. In *EUROCON 88*.

Ash, G.R. (1998). *Dynamic routing in telecommunications networks*. McGraw-Hill.

Ash, G.R. and Chemouil, P. (2004). 20 years of dynamic routing in telephone networks: looking backward to the future. *IEEE Global Communications Newsletter*, pp. 1–4. Note: appears as insert in the October 2005 issue of *IEEE Communications Magazine*.

Awschalom, D.D, Buhrman, R.A., Daughton, J.M., Von Molnár, S., Michael L. Roukes, M.L. (2004). *Spin Electronics: Final Report*. Springer, 2004

Balston, D.M and Macario, R.C.V (Eds.) (1993). Cellular radio systems. Artech.

Barker, R. H. (1953). Group Synchronizing of Binary Digital Sequences, in *Communication Theory*. London: Butterworth, pp. 273–287.

Bellman, R. E (1958). On a routing problem. *Quarterly of Applied Mathematics*, 16, 87–90.

Beneš, V.E. (1966). Programming and Control Problems Arising from Optimal Routing in Telephone Networks, *Bell System Technical Journal*, 45, 1373.

Bennett, B (1978). Network planning and design. Telecom Australia, Technical Report ED0007.

Black, U (1999). Second generation mobile and wireless networks. Prentice-Hall.

Brutt, L (1999). *NS/EP Implications of GPS timing*. Office of the Manager National Communications Systems. Technical Notes, Vol.6: 2.

Chlebus, E (1996). Nonstationary traffic models for mobile satellite communications systems. *Proc. 7th IEEE Symposium on personal, indoor and mobile radio communications*, 442–446.

Clos, C. (1953). A Study of Non-Blocking Switching Networks. *Bell System Technical Journal*, 32, 406.

Cohn, M. and Lempel, A. (1977). On Fast M-Sequence Transforms. *IEEE Transaction of Information Theory*, 23, 135–137.

Cooper, R.B. (1990) Queueing Theory. *In* Heyman, D.P and Sobel, M.J. (eds.) *Stochastic Models*, Chap. 10, 469-518. Amsterdam: North-Holland (Elsevier).

D.155: ITU-T Recommendation D.155 (1996). *Guiding principles governing the apportionment of accounting rates in intercontinental telephone relations*. Geneva.

Dijkstra, E.W (1959) A note on two problems in connexion with graphs, *Numerische Mathematik*, 1, 269–271.

Dolil, S.A, Wong, W.C and Steele, R (1989). Teletraffic performance of highway microcells with overlay macrocell. *IEEE Journal of Select. Area Communication*, 7, 71–78.

E.164: ITU-T Recommendation E.164 (2005). The international public telecommunication numbering plan. Geneva.

E.170: ITU-T Recommendation E.170 (1992). Traffic routing. Geneva.

E.412: ITU-T Recommendation E.412 (2003). Network management controls. Geneva.

E.525: ITU-T Recommendation E.525 (1992). Designing networks to control grade of service. Geneva.

E.720: ITU-T Recommendation E.720 (1993). ISDN grade of service concept. Geneva.

Engset, T (1918). Die wahrscheinlichkeitsrechnung zur bestimmung der wahleranzahl in automatischenfernsprecha (2002mtern. *Elektrotechnische zeitschrift*, 39:31, 304–306.

Erlang, A.K. (1917). Solution of some problems in the theory of probabilities of significance in automatic telephone exchanges, *Elektrotkeknikeren*, 13.

ETS 300 599 (GSM 09.02) (1997). Mobile Application Part (MAP) specification). ETSI Recommendation.

Fan, P and Darnell, M. (1996). *Sequence design for communication applications*. NY: John Wiley.

Fujimoto, K and James, J.R (eds.) (1994). Mobile antenna systems handbook. Artech.

Gallais, F., Mallepeyre, V., Andrieu, J., Nouvet, S., Betrand, V., Beillard, B and Jecko, B (2003). Two ultra wide band applications of a new 2D broad band antenna. *Proceedings of Electromagnetic Compatibility*, St Petersburg, 219–222.

Gibbens, R.J. and Kelly, F.P. (1999). Dynamic routing in fully connected networks. *Institute of Mathematics and its Applications* (*IMA*) *Journal of Mathematical Control and Information*, 7:1, 77–111.

Gibson, J.D (ed.) (1996). The mobile communications handbook. IEEE Press.

Gold, R. (1968). Maximal Recursive Sequences with 3-valued Recursive Cross-Correlation Functions. *IEEE Transaction of Information Theory*, 154–156.

Haney, M.W. and Christensen, M.P. (1997). Sliding-banyan network performance analysis. *Applied Optics IP*, 36:11, 2334–2342.

Hernando, J.M. and Perez-Fontan, F (1999). Introduction to mobile communications engineering. Artech.

Holzmann, GJ (1991) Design and validation of computer protocols. London: Prentice-Hall.

Hunter, D.K. (2000). Switching systems, in *Encyclopedia of Information Technology*, vol. 42, supplement 27, Kent, A., Williams, J. G. and Hall, C. M. (Editors), New York: Marcel Dekker, 335–370

Inose, H., Saito, T. and Yanagisawa, Y. (1973). Evaluation of PCM Toll Switching Networks with Partial Access Pulse Shifters. *Proceedings of the Seventh International Teletrajic Congress*, Stockholm, 63, 1.

ITU (2007). Website—http:/www.**itu**.int

Kanjilal, P. P. (1995). *Adaptive Prediction and Predictive Control*. Peter Peregrinus.

Karnaugh, M (1974). Loss of point-to-point traffic in three-stage circuit switches. *IBM Journal of Research development*, 204–216.

Kasami, T. (1966). *Weight Distribution Formula for Some Class of Cyclic Codes*. Tech. Report No. R-285, Univ. of Illinois.

Kim, Y., Kwon, Oh-Y., Han, T-D. and Mun, Y. (1996). Design and Performance Analysis of the Practical Fat Tree Network using a Butterfly Network. *Journal of Systems Architecture*, 43, 355–363.

Kolawole, M.O (2008). A method for cross-calibrating geostationary and polar orbiting satellite sensors in the infrared windows. *International Journal of Remote sensing*, 1–9.

Kolawole, M.O (2003). Radar systems, peak detection and tracking. Elsevier.

Kolawole, M.O (2002). Satellite Communication Engineering. Marcel Dekker.

M. 3010 (1996). Principles for a Telecommunications Management Network. ITU-T Recommendation.

Madou, M.J (2002). *Fundamentals of Microfabrication: The Science of Miniaturization*. London: CRC Press.

Massey, W.A. (2002). The Analysis of Queues with Time-Varying Rates for Telecommunication Models. *Telecommunication Systems*, 21:2–4, 173–204.

Nakamura, K., Hayashi, T., Tachibana, A. and Matsumoto, K (2000). Regional density functional theory for crystal growth in GaN. *Journal of Crystal Growth*, 221 (2000), 576–580.

Navstar (Navigation Satellite Executive Group), 1993. Global Positioning System Standard Positioning Service signal specification. Dept. of Defense Report, 46pp.

O.41: ITU-T Recommendation O.41 (1994). *Psophometer for use on telephone-type circuits*. Geneva.

OBSAI (2002). http://www.obsai.org/media/obsai_release_read.asp

P.79: ITU-T Recommendation P.79 (1999). *Calculation of loudness ratings for telephone sets*. Geneva.

P.561: ITU-T Recommendation P.561 (1996). *In-service, non-intrusive measurement device- voice service measurement*. Geneva.

Q.7: ITU-T Recommendation Q.7 (1993). Signalling systems to be used for international automatic and semi-automatic telephone network. Geneva.

Q.76: ITU-T Recommendation Q.76 (1995). Service procedures for Universal Personal Telecommunication - Functional modelling and information flows. Geneva.

Q.701: ITU-T Recommendation Q.701 (1993). Functional description of the message transfer part.(MTP) of Signalling System No. 7. Geneva.

Q.704: ITU-T Recommendation Q.704 (1996). Signalling network functions and messages. Geneva.

Q.705: ITU-T Recommendation Q.705 (1993). Signalling network structure. Geneva.

Q.706: ITU-T Recommendation Q.706 (1993). Signalling System No. 7- message transfer part signalling performance. Geneva.

Purser, M (1987). Computers and telecommunications networks. Blackwell.

U.7: ITU-T Recommendation U.7 (1993). Numbering schemes for automatic switching networks. Geneva.

U.11: ITU-T Recommendation U.11 (1993). Telex and gentex signalling on intercontinental circuits used for intercontinental automatic transit traffic (type C signalling). Geneva.

Un, C.K and Yoon, C.H (1996). Base station subsystems in (Gibson, J.D. Ed.) the mobile communications handbook. IEEE Press.

Rahnema, M. (1993). Overview of the GSM system and protocol architecture. *IEEE Communications Magazine*.

Redmill, F.J. and Valdar, A.R. (1990). SPC digital telephone exchanges. London: Peter Peregrinus.

Richards, D.L. (1978). *Calculation of reference equivalents and loudness ratings.* Electronics Letters, Volume 14:19, 647–649.

Royalsociety (The joint Royal Society and Royal Academy of Engineering Report) (2004). Nanoscience and nanotechnologies: opportunities and uncertainties. July. http://royalsociety.org/

Sarwate, D.V. and Pursley, M.B. (1980). Cross correlation properties of pseudorandom and related sequences. *Proceedings of the IEEE,* 68, 593–619.

Schwartz, M (1987). Telecommunications networks: protocols, modeling and analysis. Addison-Wesley.

Shannon, C.E (1949). Communication in the presence of noise. *Proceedings of Institute of Radio Engineers,* 37, 10–21.

Smith, S.F. (1969). Telephony and telegraphy A: an introduction to telephone and telegraph instruments and exchanges. Oxford: University Press.

Spanke, R.A. (1987). Architectures for guided-wave optical switching systems. *IEEE Communication Magazine,* 25, 42–48.

Steele, R (1992). Introduction to digital cellular radio in Steele, R (Ed.) Mobile radio communications. Pentech.

Steele, R and Nofal, M (1992). Teletraffic performance of microcellular of macrocellular personal communications networks. *IEE Proc.-I,* 139:4.

Stoll, R., Plowman, T., Winick, D. and Morris, A (2002). Integrated modeling of optical MEMS subsystems. *Proceedings of the 2002 International Conference on Modeling and Simulation of Microsystems, I,* 132-135.

Tobagi, F. A., Kwok, T. and Chiussi, F. M. (1991). Architecture, performance, and implementation of the tandem banyan fast packet switch. *IEEE Journal on Selected Areas in Communications,* 9, 1173–1193.

Wilkinson, R.I. (1956): Theories for toll traffic engineering in the USA. *Bell System Technical Journal,* Vol. 35.

Wysocki, B.J. and Wysocki, T. (2002). Modified Walsh-Hadamard sequences for DS CDMA wireless systems. *International Journal of Adaptive Control Signal Processing,* 16, 589–602.

Yurcik, W. (1999). Adaptive Multi-Layer Network Survivability: A Unified Framework for Countering Cyber-Terrorism, Proceedings of the Workshop on Countering Cyber-Terrorism, Information Sciences Institute/USC.

GLOSSARY OF TERMS

Circuit switching : A framework where a physical circuit is established between two-terminating endpoints of a switched communications network enabling a communication path there between.

CPU : Stands for the 'Central Processing Unit': a processor that performs logical functions central to system computation.

Crankback : A backtracking procedure used when a connection setup request is blocked because a node along a selected path cannot accept the request due to insufficient resources.

DCME : Stands for 'Digital Circuit Multiplication Equipment': voice compression equipment that is installed at either end of a long-distance link with echo cancellers.

Downlink : A communications link for signals coming from a satellite to the earth station.

FIFO : First in first out: an abstraction in ways of organizing and manipulation of data relative to time and prioritization.

Leased line : A dedicated line connecting two locations offering point-to-point reliable data communication over several bandwidth options.

MEMS : Stands collectively for *micro-electro-mechanical systems* such as optical switches, modulators, mechanical elements, sensors, actuators, and electronics on a common silicon substrate through microfabrication technology.

Multiplexing : A technique for transmitting multiple, simultaneous signals through a single communications channel (for example, multiple telephone conversations through a single wire). Two types:

Time-division multiplexing is a process where the signals are successively sampled, sent through the channel, and reconstructed at the end; frequently used in circuit switched (telephone) systems.

Frequency-division multiplexing is a process in which the signals are impressed on carriers of different frequencies; examples include radio, or TV broadcasting.

Packet switching : Packet switching refers to protocols where messages are broken up into small packets before they are sent. Each packet is transmitted individually across the network. Depending on the type of packet switching employed, the packets may follow different routes to the intended destination.

Protocol : A set of rules governing the exchange or transmission of data or traffic electronically between systems, devices or networks.

Ringdown : Occurs when the telephone at one end goes off-hook; the phone at the other end instantly rings.

132

Routing	:	The process of moving traffic from source to destination.
Teardown	:	A process by which traffic is routed through adjacent routers when the nominal path is incapable of forwarding such traffic through the interface unless the intermediate system interfacing the system is enabled.
Uplink	:	A communications link for signals coming from an earth station to the satellite.
UWB	:	Stands for 'ultra-wideband': UWB uses a portion of the electromagnetic spectrum at very low energy levels for short-range high-bandwidth communications.

INDEX

Switching 5-7, 13, 16, 17, 20, 23, 24, 26, 28,
31-34, 34-42, 46, 52-55, 59-61, 69-71, 75-79,
81, 85, 87, 93, 95, 105-108, 112, 113, 121, 125
    array 85
    butterfly 78
    circuit 60, 132
    crosspoint 77
    fabrics 75, 81, 83
    matrix 72, 75-80
    optical 85
    packet 33, 132

T

T-carrier 32
    E_1 11, 12, 29, 32-34, 63, 64
    T_1 11, 12, 29, 32-34, 63

T_3 33
Teardown 73, 133
Telephone 1, 3-10, 12-20, 22-27, 29-38, 40-44,
46-51, 53-55, 59, 61-70, 72-75, 82, 87, 90, 91,
93, 96, 97, 106-108, 113, 114, 132
Timeslot 32, 62, 64, 72, 76, 81-85
Top-down 124-126
Transceiver (see *Base Transceiver Station*)
Translation Table 76

U

Uplink 87, 89, 90-92, 133

V

VLSI 95
Visitor Location Register, VLR 71, 106, 107
VoIP 8, 17, 29
Vulnerability 26, 121